GCSE Success

Workbook

English & English Literature

John Mannion

CONTENTS

Contents

Punctuation and oral work

Writing and the media

Shakespeare

Poetry

Novels and short stories

The exams

Practice papers

Homework diary

Topic	Score
Punctuation again!	/35
End of sentence punctuation	/40
Uses for commas	/35
Speech marks	/65
Apostrophes	/35
Sentences	/35
Spellings	/15
Words often misspelt	/35
Homophones	/35
Linking words and phrases	/30
Linking words and phrases	/45
Improving writing style	/35
Speaking and listening	/26
Preparing and giving a talk	/31
Original writing	/19
Story planning & writing	/10
Non-fiction writing	/21
How to write essays	/23
Film extract assignment	/20
Film extract assignment	/35
Film extract assignment	/11
Shakespeare assignment	/5
Structure and themes	/28
Shakespeare's imagery	/20
An essay on Caliban	/15
Essay spidergrams	/21
Reading set poems	/28
Writing about poetry (EN2)	/17
Comparing poems	/10
Planning a poetry essay	/46
Writing on poetic technique	/23
Different cultural texts (EN2)	/37
Comparing cultural texts (EN2)	/33
Novels and short stories	/35
Novels and short stories	
Novels and short stories	/19
Literary technique (EN2)	/33
Themes, mood, atmosphere (EN2)	/11
Short stories	/15
Exam technique	/31
GCSE Practice Paper 1	/27
GCSE Practice Paper 2	/27
GCSE Practice Paper 3	/40

Exam hints

There are two major ways to revise for English:

- Studying your set texts – this should be active rather than passive. Make notes; don't just read things through.
- Practising key skills – ideally you should do this under timed conditions so you can cope better in the exam.

Planning

- Find out the dates of your exams and make an examination and revision timetable.
- Make sure you know which texts are required for each exam. If you have revised a text in class, write down the key points from memory and then check them against your notes.
- If you have completed a practice piece, look most carefully at areas that need improving.

Revising

- Revise in short bursts of about 30 minutes, followed by a short break.
- Learn facts from your exercise books, notebooks and Success guide.
- Do the multiple choice and quiz-style questions in this book and check your solutions to see how much you know.
- Once you feel confident that you know the topic, do the examination-style questions in this book. Highlight the key words in the question, plan your answer and then go back and check that you have answered the question.
- Make a note of any topics that you do not understand and go back through the notes again.
- Use the homework diary to keep track of the topics you have covered, and your scores.

Getting ready for the examination

- Read the instructions carefully and do what you are asked to do: if there are five marks you'll probably have to give five details, and so on.
- Pay particular attention to such things as layout and images in the Media text on Paper 1.
- Skim texts first to get a general idea, then scan for details.
- In the reading paper do not get bogged down on one question. You will gain most marks if you attempt all questions.
- Remember to use the Point, Example, Comment rule when commenting on texts.
- Know your texts. That way you won't waste time looking for quotations. Keep quotations short and to the point.
- Last but not least: don't panic! If you've followed the advice above, you'll certainly have done your best.

Good luck!

Punctuation again!

A

For each of the sentences below, choose the one that is correctly punctuated.

1
a) We went to watch rem at the nec last february.
b) We went to watch Rem at the Nec last February.
c) We went to watch REM at the NEC last february.
d) We went to watch REM at the NEC last February. **(1 mark)**

2
a) Dont move she shouted!
b) 'Don't move!' she shouted.
c) Don't move, she shouted.
d) 'Don't move,' she shouted. **(1 mark)**

3
a) Simon Armitages poems aren't very difficult to understand.
b) Simon Armitage's poems arent very difficult to understand.
c) Simon Armitage's poems aren't very difficult to understand.
d) Simon Armitages' poems aren't very difficult to understand **(1 mark)**

4
a) However you looked at it from the wrong point of view.
b) However you looked at it, from the wrong point of view.
c) However, you looked at it, from the wrong point of view.
d) However, you looked at it from the wrong point of view. **(1 mark)**

5
a) 'Where,' asked Emma, 'did you leave your coat?'
b) 'Where?' asked Emma, 'did you leave your coat.'
c) 'Where' asked Emma, 'Did you leave your coat?'
d) 'Where,' asked Emma, 'did you leave you're coat?' **(1 mark)**

Score / 5

B

There are ten punctuation errors in the following paragraph. Circle the errors and write out the correct words.

It was almost ten oclock when I woke up. My alarm clock was connected by radio to some sort of N.A.T.O. supercomputer and was guaranteed accurate to one millionth of a second per century. Unfortunately I forgot to turn it on before I went to sleep. 'Great.' I said to myself as I rushed down the stairs, 'thats just what I need.' Fortunately for me, the buses arent very crowded at that time in the morning and I got to work in less than half an hour.

'Ah, Mr Anderson,' said my boss, 'working flexi-time are we.

'Sorry,' I murmured, 'I was at the dentists.'

'Well, if youd let us know in advance,' he said as he wandered off.

(10 marks)

Score / 10

C This is a coursework practice question. Plan your answer here and write your response on separate paper.

Original writing coursework

Write a story suitable for teenagers on one of the following topics:

- The prisoner
- A difficult case
- Lost

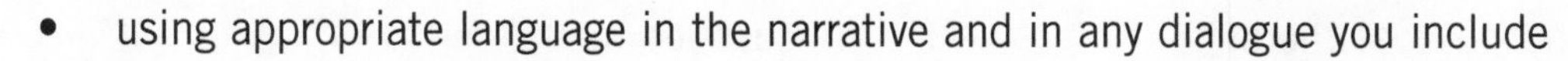

You should think about:

- making your story interesting for its intended audience
- how your story is structured
- using appropriate language in the narrative and in any dialogue you include
- using a variety of sentences and paragraphs
- correct spelling
- correct punctuation.

Score / 20

For more on this topic see pages 6–7 of your Success Guide.

Total score / 35

How well did you do? ✗ 0–7 Try again 8–18 Getting there 19–27 Good work 28–35 Excellent! ✓

End of sentence punctuation

A

Choose just one answer: a, b, c or d.

1 Which of the following does not use a semi-colon correctly?

a) Three people slept in the haunted house; none of them returned unscathed.
b) Jared made a list: matches for the fire; a book to read; extra chocolate and a torch.
c) Michaela went for a walk; Ian had a bath.
d) MACBETH: Thou canst not say I did it; never shake thy gory locks at me. **(1 mark)**

2 Which of the following sentences does not use a colon correctly?

a) I wondered if anybody was there: I went to see.
b) Everyone gathered in the hall: the cook, the butler, the two maids and the footman.
c) Prospero says: 'We are such stuff as dreams are made on.'
d) That day they appointed: a new manager; a new deputy manager and two machinists.
(1 mark)

3 Which punctuation mark is commonly replaced by a dash?

a) the colon
b) the semi-colon
c) both colons and semi-colons
d) semi-colons in lists **(1 mark)**

4 Which punctuation mark is not followed by a capital letter?

a) the full stop
b) the semi-colon
c) exclamation mark
d) question mark **(1 mark)**

5 A rhetorical question does not:

a) begin with 'what' or 'where'
b) require a question mark
c) have to be followed by a capital letter
d) require an answer **(1 mark)**

Score /5

B

The following paragraph is unpunctuated. Rewrite it using correct punctuation.

almost all of the people in charge the captain the first mate the chief petty officer and the other senior members of the crew were surprised when the news came through the ship was sinking if they had been down in the engine room they would have had a very different view of things the surprise was not that the ship was sinking but that it had ever floated in the first place when the captain found me I was knee deep in water is there anything we can do he said I paused for a second or two and then said man the lifeboats

(20 marks)

Score /20

C

This is an exam preparation question. Answer all parts of the question on separate sheets of paper.

The purpose of punctuation is to make your writing as clear as possible to the reader. The following sentences are ambiguous. Repunctuate them so that they make sense. Do not add, delete or replace any of the words.

1. **Because of his unreliability the play was delayed.**
2. **Ferdinand Magellan was the first man to sail round the world he discovered the Straits of Magellan in 1520.**
3. **Frances put the plant on the windowsill so it could get more sun.**
4. **Gemma is a very reliable student she never misses deadlines.**
5. **Healthy eating is good for you it should not be overdone.**
6. **I did not go on the outing instead I went to see a film.**
7. **I was so tired I had worked solidly for three hours.**
8. **King Charles walked and talked ten minutes after his head was cut off.**
9. **Please report to the office if you have any of the following notes of absence dinner money.**
10. **Science is a difficult subject many students hate it.**
11. **Stephen the boy with the black coat took the ball.**
12. **There was only one problem Henry knew the answer.**
13. **After we ate the neighbours came to see us.**
14. **Wherever I go my friend the doctor goes with me.**
15. **Nothing has happened since nothing could happen.**

Score / 15

For more on this topic see pages 8–9 of your Success Guide.

Total score / 40

How well did you do? 0–8 Try again 9–20 Getting there 21–31 Good work 32–40 Excellent!

Uses for commas

A

For each of the sentences below choose the one that is correctly punctuated.

1 a) 'The Mayor of Casterbridge' is one of my favourite novels.
b) The Mayor Of Casterbridge is one of my favourite novels.
c) 'The Mayor of Casterbridge' is one of my favourite novels.
d) 'The Mayor of Casterbridge' is one of my favourite novels. **(1 mark)**

2 a) The B.B.C. did a very good adaptation of Jane Austen's 'Pride and Prejudice' recently.
b) The BBC did a very good adaptation of Jane Austens 'Pride and Prejudice' recently.
c) The BBC did a very good adaptation of Jane Austen's 'Pride and Prejudice' recently.
d) The B.B.C. did a very good adaptation of Jane Austens 'Pride and Prejudice' recently. **(1 mark)**

3 a) Nobody knows where the word dog comes from.
b) Nobody knows where the word 'dog' comes from.
c) Nobody knows where the word <dog> comes from.
d) Nobody knows where the word, dog, comes from. **(1 mark)**

4 a) The line 'Alas! Poor Yorick! I knew him, Horatio.' from Hamlet is often misquoted.
b) The line: Alas! Poor Yorick! I knew him, Horatio; from 'Hamlet' is often misquoted.
c) The line 'Alas! Poor Yorick! I knew him, Horatio.' From 'Hamlet' is often misquoted.
d) The line 'Alas! Poor Yorick! I knew him, Horatio.' from 'Hamlet' is often misquoted. **(1 mark)**

5 a) The first sentence of Dickens's Bleak House is the single word 'November'.
b) The first sentence of Dickens' Bleak House is the single word 'November'.
c) The first sentence of Dickens 'Bleak House' is the single word: November.
d) The first sentence of Dickens' 'Bleak House' is the single word 'November.' **(1 mark)**

Score /5

B

The following piece of writing has ten errors involving punctuation. Write it out correctly.

The opening line of Tennysons poem the eagle is very striking.
'He clasps the crag with crooked hands'
The most noticeable thing about it is the use of the word hands where the reader might have expected something like talons or claws. The second thing that makes the line striking is the alliteration on the letter c. The repeated cs give the line a harsh sound which is in keeping with the eagles harsh environment.

....

....

....

....

.... **(10 marks)**

Score /10

This is a GCSE-style question.
Write your answer on separate sheets of paper.

Discussing a poem

Write a commentary on the following poem. Remember to use quotations to back up your points and to lay these out correctly.

The Eagle

He clasps the crag with crooked hands;
Close to the sun in lonely lands,
Ring'd with the azure world, he stands.
The wrinkled sea beneath him crawls;
He watches from his mountain walls,
And like a thunderbolt he falls.

Alfred Tennyson

Score / 20

For more on this topic see page 10 of your Success Guide.

Total score / 35

How well did you do? ✗ 0–7 Try again 8–18 Getting there 19–27 Good work 28–35 Excellent! ✓

Speech marks

A

Choose just one answer: a, b, c or d.

1 Inverted commas are not used to show:
a) when someone is being ironic
b) when someone is speaking
c) the actual words someone said
d) when something is upside down (1 mark)

2 Direct speech is:
a) when someone addresses you personally
b) separated from the rest of a sentence by a punctuation mark
c) only used in play scripts
d) more forthright than indirect speech (1 mark)

3 Direct speech:
a) begins with a capital letter
b) only starts with a capital letter if it is preceded by a full stop
c) carries on the punctuation of the sentence that introduces it
d) is punctuated according to how it is pronounced (1 mark)

4 When writing down direct speech you should always:
a) start each thing said on a new line
b) begin a new line for each new speaker
c) indent your paragraphs
d) make it clear who is speaking by using a statement marker (1 mark)

5 Indirect speech is:
a) when you say something indirectly
b) punctuated in the same way as direct speech
c) when you report what is said without using the exact words
d) punctuated using single inverted commas (1 mark)

Score /5

B

Below is a conversation that has not been punctuated or laid out properly.
Write it out correctly.

What would you like to eat asked Danielle, as she searched through the cupboards. I don't know, said Karen what have you got? Well there's pasta, rice and various sauces, said Danielle. Do you fancy Italian or Chinese? Chinese I think. OK, then what can we have with it? I think there's some salad in the fridge. That'll be fine.

"What would you like to eat?" asked Danielle, as she searched through the cupboards.
"I don't know," said Karen "What have you got?"
"Well there's pasta, rice and various sauces," said Danielle.
"Do you fancy Italian or chinese?"

Score / 25

C This is an exam preparation question. Answer both questions.

You can add variety to your writing by varying the way in which you convey speech.
In direct speech you write down the actual words spoken.
In indirect speech you report on what was said.

1 Change the following piece of indirect speech into direct speech.
My friend Clare had an argument with her dad. She was just going out and he wanted to know what time she'd be back. She said she didn't know so he got annoyed and gave her a grilling about who she was going with, where she was going, whether there'd be any boys or alcohol. Clare just gave vague answers but then she said she hadn't got time for all that and stormed out.

....

....

....

....

....

2 Change the following piece of direct speech into reported speech.
'Where's the pen I lent you?' said James.
'I thought I gave it back to you,' said Richard.
'That's what you always say!' said James. 'This is the last time I lend you anything.'
'But I did,' protested Richard. 'There it is in your pocket.'
'Oh,' said James.

....

....

....

....

....

.... **(15 marks)**

Make brief notes here on the advantages and disadvantages of direct and indirect speech.

....

....

....

....

....

....

Score / 35

For more on this topic see page 11 of your Success Guide.

Total score / 65

How well did you do? ✗ 0–13 Try again 14–33 Getting there 34–50 Good work 51–65 Excellent! ✓

Apostrophes

A

Choose just one answer: a, b, c or d.

1 Which of the following is not a possessive pronoun?

a) his
b) it's
c) mine
d) theirs **(1 mark)**

2 Which of the following possessive plurals is correctly punctuated?

a) the childrens' game
b) the Jone's house
c) the women's team
d) the Charles Dicken's Museum **(1 mark)**

3 Which of the following apostrophes is incorrect?

a) I'm going out at eight o'clock.
b) Hannas' friend is called Martha.
c) Where'd you leave your coat?
d) The house hasn't been painted in years. **(1 mark)**

4 Which of the following sentences needs an apostrophe?

a) We travelled in Charles car.
b) The Shakespeares lived in Stratford-on-Avon.
c) I want to go to the Tate Modern.
d) The horses broke into a canter. **(1 mark)**

5 The boy's bikes indicates that:

a) there are several boys with a several bikes
b) there is one boy with several bikes
c) there are several boys with one bike each
d) there are several bikes all belonging to boys **(1 mark)**

Score / 5

B

The following piece of dialogue has eleven errors involving apostrophes. Write it out correctly.

Nigel Hi! Didnt know you were goin to be here
Keri Yea, well, I changed my mind didnt I?
Nigel Whend you get ere?
Keri Bout eight oclock. Couldve been earlier, dunno.
Nigel Are you and the others going to Nicks party?
Keri Yea, were thinkin about it.

....

....

....

....

....

....

....

Score / 10

C

This is an exam preparation question.
Writing dialogue

One way of showing your understanding of a text is to carry on a scene from a play or to add an extra scene. Use the space below to add an extra scene to a play that you have studied.

Name of Play ....

Characters involved ....

How your scene fits into the play. ....

....

Begin your dialogue here. ....

....

....

....

....

....

....

....

....

....

....

....

....

....

....

Score / 20

For more on this topic see pages 12–13 of your Success Guide.

Total score / 35

How well did you do? ✗ 0–7 Try again 8–18 Getting there 19–27 Good work 28–35 Excellent! ✓

Sentences

A

There are four types of sentence in English: simple, compound, complex and minor.

For each of the following identify the sentence type.

1 Alan left this morning.

a) simple b) compound
c) complex d) minor **(1 mark)**

2 Get out!

a) simple b) compound
c) complex d) minor **(1 mark)**

3 Geography and drama are my favourite subjects.

a) simple
b) compound
c) complex
d) minor **(1 mark)**

4 I didn't go to the match on Saturday, although I wanted to.

a) simple
b) compound
c) complex
d) minor **(1 mark)**

5 The water was brought slowly to the boil.

a) passive
b) active
c) vocative
d) compound **(1 mark)**

Score /5

B

Answer all questions.

1 In the sentences below, underline the conjunction being used and then label it as either coordinating or subordinating.

a) Two buses arrived but both buses were full. ....co-ordinating....
b) They won't let you in the play if you don't arrive on time. ....Subordinating....
c) We lost the match because we didn't have enough experience. ....Subordinating....
d) He could force the door or he could break in through a window. ....co-ordinating....
e) We had a really good time until the money ran out. ....Subordinating.... **(5 marks)**

2 In the following paragraph too many compound sentences have been used. Rewrite the paragraph using a variety of sentence types. (You might also wish to change some of the pronouns to proper nouns.)

It was late and it was dark and Hudd decided to call it a day and head for his car. He walked slowly as there was always a possibility of being followed in his line of work and he didn't like the idea of being jumped on in some murky car park a long way from help without even having anything to pick up and hit his assailant with. He thought about the case as he was going along and he didn't like what he was thinking as there were too many clues and too few answers. The car park was virtually deserted apart from his own car and a rather beat-up old van that was sitting in one corner with its engine running but with no obvious driver. **(5 marks)**

Score /10

C

These are exam preparation questions. Answer both questions. Continue on separate sheets of paper where necessary.

1 **Describe a place you know well. Remember to use a variety of sentence types.**

....

....

....

....

....

....

....

.... **(10 marks)**

2 **Write the opening of a detective story. Remember to use a variety of sentence types.**

....

....

....

....

....

....

....

.... **(10 marks)**

Score / 20

For more on this topic see pages 14–15 of your Success Guide.

Total score / 35

How well did you do? ✗ 0–7 Try again 8–18 Getting there 19–27 Good work 28–35 Excellent! ✓

Spellings

A

Choose just one answer: a, b, c or d.

1 The prefix 'tele-' means:
a) far
b) to do with television
c) radiant
d) long (1 mark)

2 An 'aquameter', if it existed, would be:
a) a measure of distance
b) a device for measuring water
c) a quarter of a meter
d) a flowing line of poetry (1 mark)

3 Biannual means:
a) two years long
b) a sort of plant that blooms every two years
c) a double sized edition of a magazine
d) occurring twice a year (1 mark)

4 A monoplane is:
a) a plane with only one wing
b) a plane with only one set of wings
c) a rather boring aeroplane
d) a plane with space for a single passenger (1 mark)

5 If bicephalous means 'two-headed', what does monocephalous mean?
a) a single-horned rhinoceros
b) one-headed
c) a squid-like creature with only one tentacle
d) tending to hold a single opinion (1 mark)

Score / 5

B

Use your knowledge of word families to answer the following questions.
Answer all questions in this section.

1 What is a mnemonic?

....

(2 marks)

2 Write down a mnemonic you use, or have used, to help you to remember a spelling.

....

(2 marks)

3 What is the name for words that have the same sound but different spellings?

....

(2 marks)

4 Why do these words not show up when you are using a spell check?

....

(2 marks)

5 Write down the irregular plural forms of the following words.
dwarf, hoof, shelf, knife, life, half

....

....

(2 marks)

Score / 10

C This is an exam preparation exercise. Answer all questions.

At GCSE all of your exams (except for English) have extra marks available for good spelling, punctuation and grammar. In science you will not gain the extra marks if you misspell scientific words, and so on. English is the only exam in which you lose marks for poor spelling. In the English exam you will be penalised most for misspelling common words.

1 Subject specific words

Do you have problems spelling 'parallel' in maths, 'onomatopoeia' in English or 'appeasement' in history? In the space below write down the five words that you have most trouble spelling and work out a mnemonic for each one.

Word .... Mnemonic ....

Word .... Mnemonic ....

Word .... Mnemonic ....

Word .... Mnemonic ....

Word .... Mnemonic ....

2 Homophones

The commonest spelling errors occur with homophones.

In the space below write out a rule for telling each homophone apart.

Homophone	Rule
there, their, they're	....
your, you're	....
it's, its	....
where, wear	....
were, we're	....
principal, principle	....

3 Irregular spellings – some spellings just have to be learned.

Use the Look, Cover, Write, Check method on the spellings below.

	Look	Cover	Write	Check
a) strength	....	....	....	....
b) straight	....	....	....	....
c) February	....	....	....	....
d) library	....	....	....	....
e) subtle	....	....	....	....

For more on this topic see pages 16–19 of your Success Guide.

Total score / 15

How well did you do? ✗ 0–3 Try again 4–8 Getting there 9–12 Good work 13–15 Excellent! ✓

Words often misspelt

A

Each of the sentences below has two possible spelling errors. Choose the sentence in which both words are spelt correctly.

1 a) We can't decide whether to go to the Mediteranean or the Caribbean for our holidays.
b) We can't decide whether to go to the Mediterranean or the Caribbean for our holidays.
c) We can't decide whether to go to the Mediteranean or the Carribean for our holidays.
d) We can't decide whether to go to the Mediterranean or the Caribean for our holidays. **(1 mark)**

2 a) We wouldn't recommend accommodation at that hotel.
b) We wouldn't recomend acommodation at that hotel.
c) We wouldn't recommend acommodation at that hotel.
d) We wouldn't recomend accommodation at that hotel. **(1 mark)**

3 a) I wish the Principle would practise what he preaches.
b) I wish the Principle would practice what he preaches.
c) I wish the Principal would practice what he preaches.
d) I wish the Principal would practise what he preaches. **(1 mark)**

4 a) Waiting was unecessary becuse of the good organisation.
b) Waiting was unnecesary beccause of the good organisation.
c) Waiting was unneccessary because of the good organisation.
d) Waiting was unnecessary because of the good organisation. **(1 mark)**

5 a) The weather was definately beginning to improve.
b) The weather was definitely begining to improve.
c) The weather was definitely beginning to improve.
d) The weather was definately begining to improve. **(1 mark)**

Score /5

B

The following piece of writing has ten spelling errors. Write it out correctly in the space below.

I started working in advertising because I wanted a job that was glamorous. I thought that I mite meet sum beutiful models and famous photographers. The only model I have met so far is a model of the Eiffel Tower that we used in an advertisment for some French dressing. Its not bad work, writting advertising copy all day, but is definately not as exsiting as I thought it was going to be. I sometimes get inpatient with my boss but nobodies perfect.

....

....

....

....

Score /10

C This is a GCSE-style question.

Write an article for a school magazine in which you explain some of the problems you have had with spelling and how you overcame them.

You should:

- write in a friendly and informal style
- aim for a light tone
- offer some tips that might help others

Score / 20

For more on this topic see page 18 of your Success Guide.

Total score / 35

How well did you do? ✗ 0–7 Try again 8–18 Getting there 19–27 Good work 28–35 Excellent! ✓

Homophones

A

For each of the sentences below, choose the one that is spelt correctly.

1
a) They got into there car and drove away.
b) They got into they're car and drove away.
c) They got into their car and drove away.
d) They got into thier car and drove away.
(1 mark)

2
a) You're late.
b) Your late.
c) Your' late.
d) Youre late. **(1 mark)**

3
a) Where did you buy your rainware?
b) Wear did you buy your rainware?
c) We're did you buy your rainwear?
d) Where did you buy your rainwear? **(1 mark)**

4
a) I didn't here that you were hear until yesterday.
b) I didn't hear that you were here until yesterday.
c) I didn't here that you were here until yesterday.
d) I didn't hear that you were hear until yesterday.
(1 mark)

5
a) It's the first time I've seen the dog leave it's dinner.
b) Its the first time I've seen the dog leave it's dinner.
c) It's the first time I've seen the dog leave its dinner.
d) Its the first time I've seen the dog leave its dinner. **(1 mark)**

Score / 5

B

The following piece of writing has ten spelling errors. Write it out correctly.

The new software is called 'ANYWARE'. It's a solution for the problem of mobile computer users who don't know wear they will be working from day to day. If you have ANYWARE installed it doesn't matter were you are; the software detects the local network node and does it's stuff. It works out where you are as long as youre computer is 'Bluetooth' compatible and your not to far from a node. In theory you could be driving in a car through a city and the software would keep you're network connection running by jumping from node to node. Another use might be in computers sewn into you're clothing. The network would know were you were at all times and could reroute all your electronic data to the jacket your wearing. We're thinking of calling that version of the software 'ANYWEAR'.

....

....

....

....

....

....

.... **Score / 10**

C This is a GCSE-style question.

Write a set of instructions for a common task such as making a pot of tea or tying a pair of shoelaces. You should write in a friendly and informal style, addressing your reader as 'you'.

....

....

....

....

....

....

....

....

....

....

....

....

....

....

....

....

....

....

....

Score / 20

For more on this topic see page 19 of your Success Guide.

Total score / 35

How well did you do? ✗ 0–7 Try again 8–18 Getting there 19–27 Good work 28–35 Excellent! ✓

Linking words and phrases

A

Choose just one answer: a, b, c or d.

1 A paragraph should contain:
a) at least three sentences
b) a main idea
c) a mixture of ideas
d) a concluding sentence **(1 mark)**

2 Well organised paragraphs contain:
a) ideas linked by connectives
b) examples and illustrations
c) a topic sentence
d) all of the above **(1 mark)**

3 Topic sentences usually occur:
a) at the end
b) anywhere that is appropriate
c) in the middle
d) at the beginning **(1 mark)**

4 Which of the following is not a sequencing connective?
a) and
b) eventually
c) unless
d) subsequently **(1 mark)**

5 Some linking and sequencing phrases can be overused. Which of the following is a cliché?
a) at the end of the day
b) when all's said and done
c) when it comes down to it
d) all of the above **(1 mark)**

Score /5

B

Here are some notes for a paragraph on the birth of a star. Rewrite them using linking and sequencing words.

Massive cloud of hydrogen – gravity pulls it together – hydrogen at centre gets crushed – nuclear reaction takes place – two hydrogen atoms become one helium atom – great deal of energy released – a star is born.

....

....

....

....

....

....

....

....

....

.... Score /5

C **This is an exam preparation question. Answer all parts of the question.**

Often topic sentences on their own can give you an idea of the content of a text. (You use this fact when skim-reading.)

Below are the topic sentences for a piece of descriptive writing. Complete the paragraphs.

The old house had been deserted for years.

....

....

Once I had managed to get the door to open I was able to see into the hallway.

....

....

When I progressed into the living room I began to worry that the flooring might not be safe.

....

....

After some hesitation I decided not to attempt the stairs and made my way into what must have been the library.

....

....

I was astonished by what I read in the tattered old journal.

....

....

I was just about to leave when a shelf full of novels by Dickens caught my eye; they were all arranged in alphabetical order of title except one.

....

....

So, this was the answer to the mystery.

Score /20

For more on this topic see pages 20–21 of your Success Guide.

Total score /30

How well did you do? ✗ 0–6 Try again 7–15 Getting there 16–23 Good work 24–30 Excellent! ✓

Linking words and phrases

A

Choose just one answer: a, b, c or d.

1 Which of the following words is not a linking connective?

a) firstly
b) furthermore
c) in addition
d) moreover **(1 mark)**

2 Which of the following words or phrases can be used to show an opinion?

a) above all
b) it would seem
c) for example
d) furthermore **(1 mark)**

3 Which word below is best suited for ordering a piece of writing?

a) except
b) naturally
c) therefore
d) firstly **(1 mark)**

4 Which of the following words or phrases can be used to compare?

a) in contrast
b) subsequently
c) similarly
d) significantly **(1 mark)**

5 Which of the following words works best in a conclusion?

a) nevertheless
b) throughout
c) notwithstanding
d) furthermore **(1 mark)**

Score / 5

B

The following paragraph is poorly sequenced. Write a better organised account.

Making a cup of tea isn't all that difficult. You pour the tea from the pot into a cup and add milk. Some people like to warm the pot before adding the hot water and some people like to put the milk in the cup first. Then you add sugar if you like it. Obviously you need to have all these things ready beforehand.

....

....

....

....

.... **Score / 10**

C

This is a GCSE-style question. Answer all parts of the question. Continue on separate sheets of paper where necessary.

Write a description of a job you have undertaken. This could be a single project or your regular part-time occupation. Include the following sections:

- what you did – use sequencing words here
- how you did it – provide examples here
- whether you were successful – express your opinions in this section
- what you learned – this will be your conclusion

What I did

....

....

....

....

....

How I did it

....

....

....

....

....

Whether I was successful

....

....

....

....

....

What I learned

....

....

....

....

....

Score / 30

For more on this topic see pages 20–21 of your Success Guide.

Total score / 45

How well did you do? 0–9 Try again 10–23 Getting there 24–35 Good work 36–45 Excellent!

Improving writing style

A

Choose just one answer: a, b, c or d.

1 Short sentences can be used:

a) to build tension
b) to show that you have control of sentence punctuation
c) to move the story on quickly
d) to start a story slowly **(1 mark)**

2 Which of the following is not a cliché?

a) Clichés should be avoided like the plague.
b) The use of clichés leaves much to be desired.
c) A cliché is a phrase that is no longer outré.
d) You should leave no stone unturned in eliminating clichés. **(1 mark)**

3 Brevity is:

a) a goal much to be desired
b) one of the key elements in a mature style
c) apposite on almost any occasion
d) good **(1 mark)**

4 Which of the following is not an example of tautology?

a) puzzling mystery
b) unnecessary and redundant
c) dead and buried
d) ultimate conclusion **(1 mark)**

5 In a stylish, effective sentence the most important part is:

a) at the start
b) at the end
c) in the middle
d) where it fits best **(1 mark)**

Score /5

B

Rewrite the following paragraph to give it more tension.

The coach made its way up the hill and the day darkened around it until complete and total night had fallen. The coachman was nervous as he knew that this road was hazardous and dangerous. Only last week a coach had disappeared into thin air. Suddenly, without warning the horses reared and bucked, the creaky old coach gave up the ghost and ground to a halt. The coachman reached for the pistol he always carried with him in case of emergencies and shouted 'Who's there' into the darkness that now blanketed the land, but there was no reply or response.

....

....

....

....

....

....

....

Score /10

C

This is an exam preparation question.

Original writing

Practise improving your style. Write the opening paragraph of a story entitled: 'Why I should have stayed in bed' in the space below. Write as quickly as you can to let your ideas flow. In the second space redraft the paragraph using some of the ideas you have explored about better style.

Version 1

....

....

....

....

....

....

....

....

....

....

....

....

Version 2

....

....

....

....

....

....

....

....

....

....

....

....

Now compare the two versions. Give yourself marks up to 20 for each improvement you have made.

Score / 20

For more on this topic see pages 22–23 of your Success Guide.

Total score / 35

How well did you do? ✗ 0–7 Try again 8–18 Getting there 19–27 Good work 28–35 Excellent! ✓

Speaking and listening

A

Choose just one answer: a, b, c or d.

1 Standard English is used in most talks because:
a) it gains you more marks
b) people respond better to Standard English
c) it can be used to address the widest audience
d) it is usually associated with explanations
(1 mark)

2 A good talk is almost always:
a) about an interesting subject
b) well structured and prepared
c) funny
d) informative (1 mark)

3 The three oral tasks are:
a) brainstorming, speaking and listening
b) individual, group and drama
c) speech, drama and elocution
d) verbal, aural and contextual
(1 mark)

4 A good way to give a fluent talk is:
a) to write it out completely and learn it off by heart
b) to make sure it has a beginning, middle and end
c) to write key phrases on pieces of card as prompts
d) to choose a subject you know really well
(1 mark)

5 Which of the following is the most important factor when delivering a successful talk?
a) matching the subject of your talk with your audience
b) providing opportunities for audience interaction
c) standing up straight
d) appearing relaxed and confident (1 mark)

Score /5

B

Below is a transcript of a part of a talk given by a student.

Read it carefully and answer the question that follows.

Well ... the ... the Island in *Lord of the Flies* is a sort of laboratory that William Golding has set up. It's like he said, 'What would really happen if a group of boys was ... were stranded on a desert island. He couldn't find out by putting a group of real boys on a real island so he wrote the novel as a ... thought experiment. He decided on that ... and he let things take their course as any scientist would. Once the boys were up and running – or not as the case may be – he introduced new elements to the basic formula to see what would happen.

So ... the biggest challenge he gave to the kids was the beast.

It's interesting, innit, that the beast appeared in the boys' heads before it was given form by the dead parachutist. What I'm saying is that the beast is really the boys' fear and all ... all the things that go wrong on the island are 'cause of fear.

This ... is bad news for the rest of us. Golding reckons that fear is what makes any group of people hostile and aggressive. Just as the boys on the island can't get on because of fear ... people in the world can't get on because of fear. It's no coincidence, is it, that the boys are stranded on the island because the adults are having a nuclear war. Er ... that's it.

Make five suggestions that would improve this speech.

Score /5

C

These are exam preparation questions. Answer both questions.

1 **Below are some prompt cards on genetically modified foods. Unfortunately the speaker dropped the cards and they are in the wrong order. Can you rearrange them? Number the cards 1–6 to show their correct order.**

Genetically modified foods

- what they are
- how they are made
- give examples – soya, tomatoes, seed rape
- describe government trials

Advantages of genetically modified food

- disease resistance
- tolerance of certain weed killers – makes care of fields easier
- higher yields – especially in developing countries
- 'better', more consistent product for consumer

My opinion

- importance of scientific development
- need for proper controls
- need to feed the world
- any questions?

Arguments for

- growing world population – must do something to feed them
- new and exciting technology – might have other advantages – e.g. medicinal plants
- the cat is out of the bag – technology is available – somebody will use it – might as well be under controlled conditions

Problems with genetically modified foods

- genetics very complicated – we don't know what full effect of modification might be
- 'genetic spread' – GM plants will cross fertilise with wild plants – new unintended results
- cross species spread – e.g. weed-killer tolerance might spread to weeds – superweeds

Arguments against

- unforeseen side-effects – things look OK in the lab but not in the real world – e.g. thalidomide
- danger of superweeds, etc
- just a way of making profit – GM foods are copyrighted – same companies control weed killers
- other ways of increasing food yields are available

(6 marks)

2 **Give a talk based on these notes.** (10 marks)

Score / 16

For more on this topic see pages 24–27 of your Success Guide.

Total score / 26

How well did you do? 0–5 Try again 6–13 Getting there 14–20 Good work 21–26 Excellent!

Preparing and giving a talk

A

Choose just one answer: a, b, c or d.

1 Giving a talk requires you to:
a) speak in standard English at all times
b) learn your words off by heart
c) plan, research and practise
d) use visual aids and spider diagrams **(1 mark)**

2 The best way to remember your talk is to:
a) write down your main ideas on prompt cards
b) learn it off by heart
c) go over it just before you speak
d) have all your notes available **(1 mark)**

3 When you give your talk you should:
a) pause frequently so that people can keep up
b) not pause in case people interrupt
c) pause when there is a chance for a question
d) pause at the end of every sentence **(1 mark)**

4 In group talks it is important to:
a) make your own views clear
b) listen to others and add to their ideas
c) talk whenever the teacher is there to assess you
d) avoid being noticed as a show off **(1 mark)**

5 When you give your talk you should:
a) make things clear so people don't ask questions
b) only answer questions at the end
c) get your friends to ask you some easy questions
d) be prepared to answer any questions as they arise **(1 mark)**

Score /5

B

Speeches sometimes require you to speak more formally than usual.

Rewrite the following informal statements more formally.

a) If you're not sure where to go it's probably worth checking out the information desk.

....

....

b) I've always reckoned the food here was a bit iffy.

....

c) CU L8R

....

d) The film was really scary. It still gives me the creeps just thinking about it.

....

e) So she turns round to me and goes 'You leavin' now or what?' and I go 'Maybe. Depends.'

....

f) The teacher mumbled so a lot of the kids didn't get what he was saying.

....

Score /6

C

These are exam preparation questions. Answer both questions.
Continue on separate sheets of paper where necessary.

1 **Write the beginning of a speech aimed at teenagers in which you *argue* for guaranteed minimum pocket money.**

(10 marks)

2 **Write the beginning of a speech aimed at parents in which you try to *persuade* them to give their children more pocket money.**

(10 marks)

Score / 20

For more on this topic see pages 26–27 of your Success Guide.

Total score / 31

How well did you do? 0–7 Try again 8–17 Getting there 18–25 Good work 26–31 Excellent!

Original writing

A

Choose just one answer: a, b, c or d.

1 Which of the following genres are not allowed in original writing?

a) romantic fiction
b) autobiography
c) descriptive writing
d) there are no restrictions on genre **(1 mark)**

2 In your original writing coursework you should aim for:

a) brief accounts
b) convincing and concise writing
c) long projects
d) at least a thousand words **(1 mark)**

3 Original writing:

a) must be completely original and not related to any other parts of the course
b) may emerge from work done in other parts of the course
c) should include some oral preparation
d) should not be based on things you have read independently **(1 mark)**

4 If you decide to submit poetry, it is a good idea to:

a) make sure it rhymes
b) write one long poem of about 1000 words
c) include a brief commentary on the poems
d) write in ballad quatrains **(1 mark)**

5 Which of the following is most important for gaining good marks in original writing?

a) originality
b) perfect spelling
c) varied sentence structure
d) well-focused and appropriate writing **(1 mark)**

Score /5

B

Match the following sentences to their genre.

1 Marsha hacked down the last wall of creepers and was rewarded by a sight unseen for a thousand years; the lost Temple of Uxor.

2 I was born, according to my parents, on a stormy night in November and storms have been pretty much part of my life ever since.

3 The Fleet river is one of the lost rivers of London. It still flows and it still feeds into the Thames, but very few people have actually seen it.

4 The dead man walked towards me, grinning through lips that were already starting to rot away.

5 The doctor injected the nanobots into my arm. 'Well, that should keep you fit and healthy for another seventy five years,' he said.

6 Moving through the empty spaces.
Unmoved by all the empty faces.

7 I grabbed him by the neck and pushed him against the wall. He wasn't pleased. 'Just a few questions,' I said.

A Travel writing

B Science fiction

C Detective fiction

D Autobiography

E Poetry

F Horror

G Adventure

Score /14

C

This is an exercise about adding an extra chapter to a known text. Use the framework below to help you to plan your answer. Answer all parts of the question. Continue on separate sheets of paper where necessary.

Identify a gap in the story. What happened just before the events of the text? What happened after?

....

....

....

....

Which characters are involved? What do we know about them? What would we like to know?

....

....

....

....

What will you add to the text? A happier ending? More detail about a character?

....

....

....

....

What is the style of the original? How much dialogue is used? How much description? Does it use formal or informal language?

....

....

....

....

How is the original written? Long or short sentences/paragraphs? Adjectival descriptions? Similes, metaphors and other literary devices?

....

....

....

....

For more on this topic see pages 30–31 of your Success Guide.

Total score / 19

How well did you do? ✗ 0–4 Try again 5–10 Getting there 11–15 Good work 16–19 Excellent! ✓

Story planning & writing

A

Choose just one answer: a, b, c or d.

1 The plot of a story consists of:
a) its main events
b) its main events and the connections between them
c) an evil plan hatched by one of the characters
d) your plan of the story before you write it
(1 mark)

2 Which of the following is not a fiction genre?
a) romance
b) science fiction
c) detective
d) biography (1 mark)

3 The hook of a story is:
a) the thing that it is really about
b) the twist in its tail
c) its moral or message
d) an interesting beginning (1 mark)

4 First person narration involves:
a) the use of an 'I' point of view
b) only one person telling the story
c) telling the reader what goes on in the minds of the characters
d) using a single character
(1 mark)

5 One advantage of third person narration over first person narration is:
a) you can tell the story in different voices
b) you can give the thoughts of more than one character
c) it is less complicated than first person narration
d) it helps create suspense
(1 mark)

Score / 5

B

Read the following paragraph from the beginning of a science fiction story and then answer the question.

I woke up and had my breakfast. I had toast I think. Then I got up and went to the office. As usual there was a queue waiting for me but I tried not to notice how strange some of them looked as I walked past them into my office. The first alien who walked through my door was called Adj. He was from Alpha Centauri. He didn't have too many eyes and moved around on two legs – in poor light he would have passed for human.
'Greetings!' he said. (What is it with aliens and saying 'Greetings!'? Can't they say 'Hi' like everybody else?)
'Hi,' I said, 'What's your problem?'
'Well,' he began …

Suggest five ways in which this story could be improved.

....

....

....

....

....

....

....

....

....

....

Score / 5

C **This is an exam preparation question. Answer all parts of the question. Continue on separate sheets of paper where necessary.**

Writing fiction

Use the following template to make notes to plan a piece of fiction.
Characters – who is involved? What are their relationships?

....

....

Main character

....

....

Other character

....

....

Setting – where does the story take place?

....

....

When? – what time period?

....

....

Genre – what kind of fiction?

....

....

Target audience – how to appeal to them?

....

....

Structure

....

....

Beginning – set up story, characters and setting. Introduce problem

....

....

Middle – problem reaches a crisis

....

....

End – problem solved

....

....

Hook – start at interesting point? Start at middle/end and then use flashback?

....

....

For more on this topic see pages 32–33 of your Success Guide.

Total score / 10

How well did you do? ✗ 0–2 Try again 3–5 Getting there 6–8 Good work 9–10 Excellent! ✓

Non-fiction writing

A

Choose just one answer: a, b, c or d.

1 Which of the following genres is non-fiction?
a) thriller b) autobiography
c) romance d) action (1 mark)

2 What should you always consider when you are writing non-fiction?
a) providing detailed evidence
b) using quotations
c) audience, form and purpose
d) using persuasive language (1 mark)

3 Which of the following is not an aspect of good non-fiction writing?
a) matches audience with purpose
b) uses wide-ranging vocabulary
c) can be both elaborate and concise
d) uses a clear and readable font (1 mark)

4 Which of the following is usually a form of non-fiction writing?
a) letter
b) sonnet
c) novel
d) dramatic monologue (1 mark)

5 Non-fiction writing is tested in:
a) coursework only
b) exam only
c) both coursework and exam
d) either coursework or exam (1 mark)

Score /5

B

The following piece of non-fiction writing is supposed to be a newspaper report. As a newspaper report, it has at least eight faults. Can you spot them?

A dog rescued a boy from drowning at a local beauty spot

Yesterday a dog rescued a boy from drowning at Willow Pond. The boy's name was William Smith but you will have to read the rest of this article to find out the dog's name.

William had been swimming in Willow Pond when he caught his foot on a branch or something and couldn't get to the shore. 'Help! Help!' he shouted, but there was no one around. After several minutes of trying to free his foot, William thought he was going to drown as he could no longer keep his head above water. But then along came the mysterious dog who was able to support him in the water while he freed his foot. According to the medallion on his collar, the dog's name was Max.

Score /8

C

This is a GCSE-style question. Answer all parts of the question. Continue on separate sheets of paper where necessary.

Writing a blog

Fill in the following plan to help you to plan a blog for a website such as MySpace.

Planning	
Who is your audience? (e.g. people your age)	What is your purpose? (e.g. to review music, to amuse your friends)
Which subjects will you mostly deal with? (e.g. films, animal rights, your life)	How often do you plan to update your blog?
What kind of language will you use? Formal? Informal? Slang?	Will you be mostly concerned with facts – as in a diary – or with ideas and opinions?
Will you include illustrations or links to other websites?	How will you respond to comments?

Sample content
Use this space to write a sample entry.

Score / 8

For more on this topic see pages 34–35 of your Success Guide.

Total score / 21

How well did you do? ✗ 0–5 Try again 6–11 Getting there 12–16 Good work 17–21 Excellent! ✓

How to write essays

A

Choose just one answer: a, b, c or d.

1 A well-planned essay:
a) has a logical structure
b) uses connectives to show how ideas are related
c) makes good use of evidence
d) addresses the key words and phrases in the question and answers them **(1 mark)**

2 Literary essays should contain:
a) quotations
b) quotations and close references to the text
c) points backed up by quotations and comments
d) quotations and comments **(1 mark)**

3 The conclusion of an essay should:
a) restate your arguments
b) sum up your arguments and say what has been learned
c) restate the arguments and point the way to further questions
d) give the essay a sense of finality **(1 mark)**

4 Effective use of quotations means:
a) quoting the exact word or phrase that has led to a conclusion
b) providing enough of a context to let the reader judge the quotation
c) choosing words and phrases that are familiar to the reader
d) commenting appropriately on a text **(1 mark)**

5 A reference to a text is most appropriate:
a) when you can't remember the exact quotation
b) when the actual language used by the author is not important
c) when you are making a general point
d) when there isn't time to tell the full story **(1 mark)**

Score / 5

B

Read the following passage from a student's essay and then answer the questions that follow on separate paper.

The main message, then, in *To Kill a Mockingbird* is not to judge by appearances. Scout and Jem learn that the monsters of their childhood, Boo and Mrs Dubose, have stories of their own and the town has learned, a little, that you should not judge a man by his colour. The key to all of this is sympathy for outsiders and loners; as Atticus says you should never judge someone unless you have 'walked around in his shoes'. (This message works most of the time but we shouldn't forget that Tom Robinson got into trouble for being too sympathetic.) The final part of the book, when Scout sees her own childish world from Boo's point of view, also tells us that we should try to see ourselves from other people's points of view.

1 Where do you think this passage comes from in the essay? **(1 mark)**

2 Identify a quotation. Do you think it has been used effectively? **(2 marks)**

3 Identify a close reference to the text. Do you think it has been used effectively? **(2 marks)**

4 Do you think this piece of writing works well? Give reasons for your answer. **(2 marks)**

5 Suggest one improvement to this passage. **(1 mark)**

Score / 8

C **This is a GCSE-style question. Answer all parts of the question. Continue on separate sheets of paper where necessary.**

Writing a literary essay

Identify one character from a novel you have studied and explain how the character is changed by his or her experiences. Use the headings below as starting points for your character analysis.

What the character is like at the beginning of the novel

....

....

....

....

....

....

The important incidents that cause a change

....

....

....

....

....

....

What the character is like at the end

....

....

....

....

....

....

How the author helps us to see and understand the change

....

....

....

....

....

....

Score / 10

For more on this topic see pages 36–37 of your Success Guide.

Total score / 23

How well did you do? ✗ 0–5 Try again 6–12 Getting there 13–18 Good work 19–23 Excellent! ✓

Film extract assignment

A

Choose just one answer: a, b, c or d.

1 For you media coursework you will need to:
a) imagine, explore and entertain
b) analyse, review and comment
c) inform, explain and describe
d) discuss, argue and persuade **(1 mark)**

2 Which of the following is not a media text?
a) novel
b) film
c) newspaper
d) advertisement **(1 mark)**

3 A key light is:
a) a special light that allows access to a scene
b) the most important light in a scene
c) the main source of light in a scene
d) the opposite of a backlight **(1 mark)**

4 Diegetic sound is:
a) a form of stereo sound
b) sound produced in the world of the film
c) background sound
d) another word for musical soundtrack **(1 mark)**

5 When there is no sound in a film it might be:
a) because it is an old-fashioned silent film
b) because the actors are not talking
c) to give the audience a pause between scenes
d) because the director wishes to create tension **(1 mark)**

Score /5

B

Match the following props to the film type.

Props

1 Wigs, gloves, horse-drawn carriage
2 Stagecoach, stetson, Colt 45 revolver
3 Teleporter, ray-gun, time machine
4 Gravestone, wooden stake, crucifix
5 Miniature camera, satellite surveillance, fast car

Film type

A Science fiction
B Spy film
C Horror film
D Western
E Historical drama

Score /5

C This is an exam preparation question. Write the *mise-en-scène* for a scene in a film; that is a description of what the audience would see at the beginning of the scene.

Remember to be as accurate as possible and mention as many things as you can to help the director to put your ideas on film.

Score / 10

For more on this topic see pages 38–39 of your Success Guide.

Total score / 20

How well did you do? 0–5 Try again 6–11 Getting there 12–16 Good work 17–20 Excellent!

Film extract assignment

A

Choose just one answer: a, b, c or d.

1 Which of the following is not a traditional film shot?
a) extreme close-up
b) reduction shot
c) low angle shot
d) dolly shot (1 mark)

2 High angle shots:
a) make characters look more powerful
b) make characters look up towards the camera
c) give a good overview of the scene
d) make characters look less powerful (1 mark)

3 Which of the following is not a camera movement?
a) panning
b) swan shot
c) rolling shot
d) crane shot (1 mark)

4 Which of the following shots is useful for showing a character's emotions?
a) panning shot
b) total shot
c) close-up
d) two shot (1 mark)

5 What does a POV shot do?
a) establishes a scene
b) makes a character seem more important
c) shows the scene from a character's point of view
d) focuses the audience's attention on one character (1 mark)

Score / 5

B

Below is an extract from a film script. Read it carefully and think about the shots and camera movements that the scene would require.

We are in New York. We see the tall buildings in the background and the smart apartments on the edge of Central Park. We zoom in towards the window of one of them.

We now see the interior of one of the apartments. It is well furnished and brightly lit. There is a fire in the grate. Beside the fire is an old-fashioned wing chair with a man sitting in it. He does not move. We notice that he is holding a brandy glass loosely in his fingers. The glass is empty and its contents are spilled across the floor.

This scene involves at least six shots.

Write down your suggestions for each shot in the spaces below.

1 ....

2 ....

3 ....

4 ....

5 ....

6 ....

Score / 6

C **This is an exam preparation question.**

Use the storyboard below to plan the opening few moments of a film. Your film can be on any subject.

Remember to use sound, dialogue and a variety of shots in your scene.

Storyboard

	Type of shot: Dialogue/Sound:		Type of shot: Dialogue/Sound:
	Type of shot: Dialogue/Sound:		Type of shot: Dialogue/Sound:
	Type of shot: Dialogue/Sound:		Type of shot: Dialogue/Sound:
	Type of shot: Dialogue/Sound:		Type of shot: Dialogue/Sound:

Score / 24

For more on this topic see pages 40–41 of your Success Guide.

Total score / 35

How well did you do? ✗ 0–7 Try again 8–18 Getting there 19–27 Good work 28–35 Excellent! ✓

Film extract assignment

A

Choose just one answer: a, b, c or d.

1 What is the main purpose of editing a film?
a) to remove parts that may not be suitable for the audience
b) to make sure that the film flows well
c) to allow changes in the film after it has been shot
d) to make sure it is realistic (1 mark)

2 What is the commonest type of film cut?
a) the jump cut b) fade out
c) dissolve d) straight cut (1 mark)

3 The main use of montages is to:
a) produce a creepy feeling
b) indicate the end of an episode
c) provide a great deal of information quickly
d) blend scenes together (1 mark)

4 Wipe cuts are most suitable for:
a) comedies b) tragedies
c) romances d) historical dramas (1 mark)

5 Which other member of a film crew works closely with the editor?
a) cameraman b) electrician
c) director d) producer (1 mark)

Score / 5

B

Imagine you are a film editor. What type of cuts or edits would you use in the following scenes?

1 An important conversation between two characters.

....

....

2 An action-packed scene involving many different actions and characters.

....

....

3 A flashback when a character recalls earlier events.

....

....

4 A move to a new location in an adventure film.

....

....

5 A scene where an important character dies.

....

....

6 The shift from a scene featuring the hero to a scene featuring the heroine.

....

....

Score / 6

C

This is a GCSE Media Coursework practice question. Answer all parts of the question.

Use the following writing frame to help you analyse a scene from a film.

Opening paragraph

The film scene I have chosen to study is for (name of film) directed by (name of director). The scene I have chosen is (brief description of scene) and it features (names of actors). I have chosen it because (mention such things as content, interesting techniques used, genre of film, unusualness and so on. Express your own opinion).

....

....

Paragraph 2

The most obvious and striking aspect of this scene is its use of (stunts, special effects, cgi graphics, animation, etc). The best example of this is when

....

The impact of this on the audience is

....

Paragraph 3

The scene is also remarkable for its use of (light, sound, music, etc.)

For example

....

The effect of this is

....

Paragraph 3

Careful study of the way this scene works reveals that it has been very cleverly (filmed, edited, etc).

For instance

....

Without this (camera work editing) the effect would be

....

Paragraph 4

The director's use of props and locations is

A good example of this is

The audience reacts to this

....

....

Paragraph 5

All together this scene works well because

....

....

Note: Use the longer writing frame in the Success Guide if you wish to write about a single scene. You can use this writing frame twice to write briefer assessments of two scenes which you can then compare.

For more on this topic see pages 42–43 of your Success Guide.

Total score / 11

How well did you do? ✗ 0–2 Try again 3–5 Getting there 6–8 Good work 9–11 Excellent! ✓

Shakespeare assignment

A

Choose just one answer: a, b, c or d.

1 Which of the following is not a feature of Shakespeare's language?

a) rhyming couplets
b) blank verse
c) Standard English
d) prose (1 mark)

2 Blank verse is:

a) unrhymed
b) mostly used in comedy
c) the kind used in birthday cards
d) used in 12-syllable lines (1 mark)

3 A good place to research Shakespeare's philosophical context is:

a) a philosophy textbook
b) a history textbook
c) a drama textbook
d) a poetry textbook (1 mark)

4 Which of the following is not a play by Shakespeare:

a) The Merchant of Venice
b) Venus and Adonis
c) The Winter's Tale
d) Antony and Cleopatra (1 mark)

5 As well as demonstrating your knowledge of a play by Shakespeare you will also need to:

a) show an understanding of his social, cultural and historical context
b) show a knowledge of Shakespearean costume conventions
c) show a knowledge of Shakespeare's dramatic career
d) show an understanding of other Elizabethan playwrights (1 mark)

Score /5

B

Fill in the following table as fully as you can with reference to the play you have studied.

There is no score for this exercise but it will help you to understand the structure of your play.

Act and its function	What happens
Act 1 Introduction	
Act 2 Problems revealed	
Act 3 Chaos/loss of harmony	
Act 4 Problems continue	
Act 5 Climax Harmony restored	

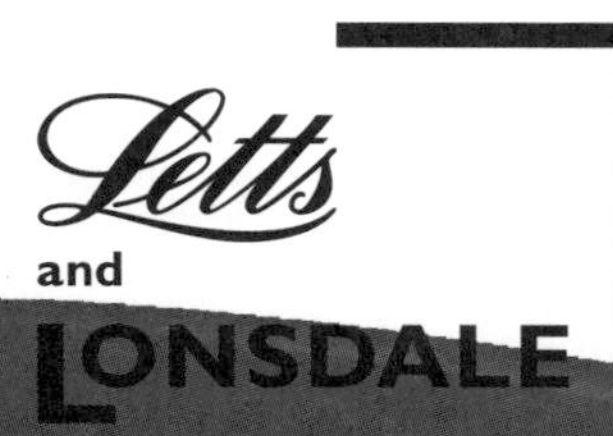

GCSE Success

Workbook Answer Booklet

English & English Literature

John Mannion

GCSE English & English Literature Answer Booklet

PUNCTUATION AGAIN!

Section A
1 d
2 b
3 c
4 d
5 a

Section B
It was almost ten o'clock when I woke up. My alarm clock was connected by radio to some sort of NATO supercomputer and was guaranteed accurate to one millionth of a second per century. Unfortunately, I forgot to turn it on before I went to sleep.
'Great!' I said to myself as I rushed down the stairs, 'That's just what I need.'
Fortunately for me the buses aren't very crowded at that time in the morning and I got to work in less than half an hour.
'Ah, Mr Anderson,' said my boss, 'working flexi-time are we?'
'Sorry,' I murmured, 'I was at the dentist's.'
'Well, if you'd let us know in advance,' he said as he wandered off.

Section C
Give yourself a mark out of 20 and have someone check your work. Remove 1 mark for every error made.

END OF SENTENCE PUNCTUATION

Section A
1 c
2 d
3 a
4 b
5 d

Section B
Almost all of the people in charge: the captain; the first mate; the chief petty officer and the other senior members of the crew, were surprised when the news came through: the ship was sinking! If they had been down in the engine room they would have had a very different view of things: the surprise was not that the ship was sinking, but that it had ever floated in the first place. When the captain found me I was knee deep in water.
'Is there anything we can do?' he said.
I paused for a second or two and then said: 'Man the lifeboats'.'

Section C
1 Because of his unreliability, the play was delayed.
2 Ferdinand Magellan was the first man to sail round the world; he discovered the Straits of Magellan in 1520.
3 Frances put the plant on the windowsill, so it could get more sun.
4 Gemma is a very reliable student; she never misses deadlines.
5 Healthy eating is good for you: it should not be overdone.
6 I did not go on the outing; instead I went to see a film.
7 I was so tired; I had worked solidly for three hours.
8 King Charles walked and talked: ten minutes after, his head was cut off.
9 Please report to the office if you have any of the following: notes of absence; dinner money.
10 Science is a difficult subject: many students hate it.
11 Stephen, the boy with the black coat, took the ball.
12 There was only one problem: Henry knew the answer.
13 After we ate, the neighbours came to see us.
14 Wherever I go my friend, the doctor, goes with me.
15 Nothing has happened, since nothing could happen

USES FOR COMMAS

Section A
1 a
2 c
3 b
4 d
5 d

Section B
The opening line of Tennyson's poem *The Eagle* is very striking.
'He clasps the crag with crooked hands'
The most noticeable thing about it is the use of the word 'hands' where the reader might have expected something like 'talons' or 'claws'. The second thing that makes the line striking is the alliteration on the letter 'c'. The repeated 'c's give the line a harsh sound which is in keeping with the eagle's harsh environment.

Section C
Give yourself a mark out of 20 and have someone check your work. Remove 1 mark for every error made.

SPEECH MARKS

Section A
1 d
2 b
3 a
4 b
5 c

Section B
'What would you like to eat?' asked Danielle, as she searched through the cupboards.
'I don't know,' said Karen, 'what have you got?'
'Well there's pasta, rice and various sauces,' said Danielle.
'Do you fancy Italian or Chinese?'
'Chinese I think.'
'OK, then what can we have with it?'
'I think there's some salad in the fridge.'
'That'll be fine.'

Section C
1 Your answer should look like the following passage. (2 marks for every speech up to a total of 20).
Clare was just going out and when her dad said: 'What time will you be back?'
Clare said: 'I don't know.'
Her father got annoyed and asked, 'Who are you going with?
'The usual people'
'Where are you going? Will there be any boys?
'How should I know?'
'Alcohol?'
'I haven't got time for all this'
Clare stormed out.
2 Your answer should look like the following passage. (1 mark for every speech reported up to a total of 15).
James asked Richard where the pen he lent him was. Richard said that he thought he'd given it back but James claimed that that's what he always said. James said it was the last time he would lend Richard anything. At this point Richard protested and said that he did give the pen back. It was in James's pocket. James was embarrassed.

APOSTROPHES

Section A
1 b
2 c
3 b
4 a
5 b

Section B
Nigel Hi! Didn't know you were goin' to be here.
Keri Yea, well, I changed my mind didn't I?
Nigel When'd you get 'ere?
Keri 'Bout eight o'clock. Could've been earlier, dunno.
Nigel Are you and the others going to Nick's party?
Keri Yea, we're thinkin' about it.

Section C
Give yourself a mark out of 20 and have someone check your work. Remove 1 mark for every error made.

SENTENCES

Section A
1 a
2 d
3 a
4 c
5 a

Section B
1 a) Two buses arrived <u>but</u> both buses were full Co-ordinating
b) They won't let you into the play <u>if</u> you don't arrive on time. Subordinating
c) We lost the match <u>because</u> we didn't have enough experience. Subordinating
d) He could force the door <u>or</u> he could break in through a window. Co-ordinating
e) We had a really good time <u>until</u> the money ran out. Subordinating
2 **Sample answer:**
It was late and it was dark. Hudd decided to call it a day and headed for his car. He walked slowly, as there was always a possibility of being followed in his line of work. He didn't like the idea of being jumped on in some murky car park a long way from help or not even having anything to pick up and hit his assailant with. Hudd thought about the case as he was going along. He didn't like what he was thinking as there were too many clues and too few answers. The car park was virtually deserted, apart from his own car and a rather beat-up old van that was sitting in one corner with its engine running but with no obvious driver.

Section C
Give yourself 10 marks for each question if you used all four types of sentence, 8 marks for three types, 6 marks for two types and 4 marks if you only used one type of sentence.

SPELLINGS

Section A
1 a
2 b
3 d
4 b
5 b

Section B
1 A mnemonic is a word, phrase or sentence that helps you to remember something.
2 2 marks for any mnemonic.

3 Homophone
4 Spell check programs only check to see if a word is correctly spelt. They can't tell if it is the right choice of word.
5 Dwarves, hooves, shelves, knives, lives, halves

Section C
For practice only.

WORDS OFTEN MISSPELT

Section A
1 b
2 a
3 d
4 d
5 c

Section B
I started working in advertising because I wanted a job that was glamorous. I thought that I might meet some beautiful models and famous photographers. The only model I have met so far is a model of the Eiffel Tower that we used in an advertisement for some French dressing.
It's not bad work, writing advertising copy all day, but is definitely not as exciting as I thought it was going to be. I sometimes get impatient with my boss but nobody's perfect.

Section C
Give yourself a mark out of 20 and have someone check your work. Remove 1 mark for every error made.

HOMOPHONES

Section A
1 c
2 a
3 d
4 b
5 c

Section B
The new software is called 'ANYWARE'. It's a solution for the problem of mobile computer users who don't know where they will be working from day to day. If you have ANYWARE installed it doesn't matter where you are; the software detects the local network node and does its stuff. It works out where you are as long as your computer is 'Bluetooth' compatible and you're not too far from a node. In theory you could be driving in a car through a city and the software would keep your network connection running by jumping from node to node. Another use might be in computers sewn into your clothing. The network would know where you were at all times and could reroute all your electronic data to the jacket you're wearing. We're thinking of calling that version of the software 'ANYWEAR'.

Section C
Give yourself a mark out of 20 and have someone check your work. Remove 1 mark for every error made.

LINKING WORDS AND PHRASES

Section A
1 b
2 d
3 d
4 c
5 d

Section B
Sample answer:
Stars are born inside massive clouds of hydrogen. Gravity pulls the molecules together until the hydrogen at the centre of the cloud gets crushed. Eventually the pressure becomes so great that a nuclear reaction begins to take place. Two hydrogen atoms become one helium atom and a great deal of energy is released in the process. In this way a star is born.

Section C
20 marks if the story reads well and is interesting. Subtract 1 mark per spelling mistake and punctuation error. Check for sentence variety.

LINKING WORDS AND PHRASES

Section A
1 a
2 b
3 d
4 c
5 b

Section B
Score 1 mark up to a total of 10 for each sequencing word or phrase you use.
Sample answer:
First of all get all the things you will need ready: a cup, a teaspoon, tea leaves or teabags, a teapot, milk and sugar. Next warm the pot with a little hot water and then add the tea. Pour in the rest of the hot water and wait for the tea to brew. When the tea is brewed put some milk into a cup and then pour in the tea. Finally, add sugar if you take it, and stir.

Section C
Give yourself 1 mark for every linking word or phrase you used apart from 'and' up to a total of 30.

IMPROVING WRITING STYLE

Section A
1 a
2 c
3 d
4 c
5 b

Section B
1 mark per change.
Sample answer:
The coach made its way up the hill. The day darkened around it until absolute night had fallen. The coachman was nervous. He knew that this road was hazardous and dangerous; only last week a coach had disappeared into thin air. Suddenly, the horses reared. The decrepit coach stopped. The coachman reached for the pistol he always carried with him and shouted 'Who's there?' into the darkness. But there was no answer.

Section C
Give yourself a mark out of 20 and have someone check your work. Remove 1 mark for every error made.

SPEAKING AND LISTENING

Section A
1 c
2 b
3 b
4 c
5 a

Section B
1 – More practice to prevent pauses at card change over.
2 – Fewer clichés.
3 – Slightly more formal: use Standard English throughout.
4 – More confidence: fewer pauses.
5 – Better planning at the end.

Section C
1 Genetically modified foods.
2 Advantages of genetically modified foods.
3 Problems with genetically modified foods.
4 Arguments for.
5 Arguments against.
6 My opinion.
(It could also go 1, 3, 2, 5, 4, 6.)

PREPARING AND GIVING A TALK

Section A
1 c
2 a
3 c
4 b
5 d

Section B
a) If you are not sure where to go consult the information desk.
b) I have always thought that the food here was a little dubious.
c) I will see you later.
d) The film was very frightening. It still disturbs me to think about it.
e) Eventually she asked me, 'Are you ready to leave?' and I replied 'Possibly.'
f) The teacher mumbled a great deal so that the students did not always understand.

Section C
Compare the two speeches and give yourself top marks if there is a noticeable difference in the formality of the language.

ORIGINAL WRITING

Section A
1 d
2 b
3 b
4 c
5 d

Section B
1 G
2 D
3 A
4 F
5 B
6 E
7 C

Section C
For practice only.

STORY PLANNING & WRITING

Section A
1 b
2 d
3 d
4 a
5 b

Section B
1 Starts off with too much boring detail
2 More description of the aliens
3 Less 'off topic' thought
4 Needs to be more exciting/ interesting
5 More sentence variety

Section C
For practice only

NON-FICTION WRITING

Section A
1 b
2 c
3 d
4 a
5 c

Section B
1 Headline should be in a larger font.
2 Headline should be short and punchy.
3 the use of 'you' (direct address) should not be used in news stories.
4 The use of 'I' should not be in news stories.
5 Suspense (keeping the dog's name until the end) is not used in news stories.
6 The use of 'or something' is too informal.
7 'Help! Help!' he shouted – this is story-telling style.
8 'The mysterious dog' – again, this is story-telling style.

Section C
Give yourself one mark if your sample content fits the criteria identified in the planning stage.

HOW TO WRITE ESSAYS

Section A
1 d
2 c
3 b
4 b
5 b

Section B
1 Near the end.
2 'walked around in his shoes' – Yes. It backs up the comment made.
3 Scout seeing the world from Boo's viewpoint – Yes. It leads on to the final comment.
4 Yes – It is summing up what has been learned from the book.
5 It could be better organised – the bracketed section looks like an afterthought.

Section C
When you have completed the essay give yourself marks for every point, example and comment you make, up to a maximum of 10.

FILM EXTRACT ASSIGNMENT

Section A
1 b
2 a
3 c
4 b
5 d

Section B
1 E
2 D
3 A
4 C
5 B

Section C
Give yourself marks for describing: character appearance (2), costumes (2), make-up (1), hair style (1), props (1), lighting and colour (1), the setting (2)

FILM EXTRACT ASSIGNMENT

Section A
1 d
2 d
3 b
4 c
5 c

Section B
Give yourself 1 mark for each shot.
1 Establishing shot – New York Skyline
2 Crane / panning shot from Central Park to apartment
3 Establishing shot – Apartment
4 Total shot – the fireplace
5 Medium shot – man in chair
6 Close-up – hand and brandy glass

Section C
Give yourself up to 3 marks per square. 1 mark each for interesting image, a variety of interesting shots and good use of sound or dialogue

FILM EXTRACT ASSIGNMENT

Section A
1 b
2 d
3 c
4 a
5 c

Section B
1 Straight cuts
2 Jump cuts
3 Fade out or dissolve
4 Wipe cut
5 Fade out
6 Dissolve

Section C
This answer can be submitted as part of a GCSE coursework assignment. Remember that you are writing to analyse, review and comment.

SHAKESPEARE ASSIGNMENT

Section A
1 c
2 a
3 b
4 b
5 a or d

Section B
For practice only.

Section C
This answer can be submitted as part of a coursework assignment.

STRUCTURE AND THEMES

Section A
1 a
2 c
3 d
4 b
5 c

Section B
Give yourself a mark for each box filled in. Typical answers might be:
The Tempest Father daughter love – Prospero and Miranda – the need for independence
Macbeth Good and Evil – Macbeth, Lady Macbeth, the Witches – One evil deed leads to another
Romeo and Juliet Young love – Romeo and Juliet – violent delights have violent ends
Henry V Kingship – Henry and his old friends – Kings cannot let their personal loyalties get in the way of justice

Section C
1. Shakespeare usually waits before introducing his main characters. We often hear something about them before we see them on stage.
2. The main problems are usually introduced at the end of Act 1 or the beginning of Act 2. In comedies these often involve mistaken identity. Tragedies usually involve the introduction of some force for evil.
3. Act 3 is usually the period of maximum confusion in comedies and maximum disruption in tragedies
4. The climax of most plays usually occurs towards the end of Act 3 or at the beginning of Act 4. Some idea of how things might be resolved is often introduced towards the end of Act 4.
5. The resolution of the play usually takes place in Act 5. Rewards and punishments are handed out and balance is restored.

SHAKESPEARE'S IMAGERY

Section A
1 d
2 b
3 a
4 a
5 c

Section B
1 It falls like gentle rain from heaven.
2 It is good for the person who gives mercy and for the person who receives it.
3 Powerful people have the ability to show great mercy.
4 It is better than any other aspect of kingship.
5 To show mercy is to act in a God-like way.

Section C
1 He is shocked and horrified.
2 She is scornful of her husband and thinks that washing away the blood will clear them of guilt.
3 He has become hardened to bloodshed. He is so involved that giving up killing is just as bad as carrying on.
4 She has become obsessed with his blood. She tries to wash it off but the memory cannot be erased.
5 In the first passage Lady Macbeth thinks that water will wash away her guilt whereas Macbeth feels that his guilt will turn all the oceans red with blood. In the second passage it is Lady Macbeth who feels that her guilt is so enormous that 'all the perfumes of Arabia' will not hide it.

AN ESSAY ON CALIBAN

Section A
1 b
2 d
3 a
4 b
5 c

Section B
1 Caliban is often tormented and teased.
2 The first speech shows Caliban's resentment and unhappiness. The second shows his awe at some of its beauties and his frustration that he cannot appreciate them all the time.
3 The first speech has a strong rhythm, particularly at the beginning when Caliban lists the things he would like to happen to Prospero, using a great deal of alliteration. The second speech has a much gentler rhythm, created by the use of simple monosyllables as in line 2 or harmonious polysyllables as in line 3. The first speech is characterised by unpleasant things such as 'fens', 'bogs' and 'painful hedgehogs'. This helps to create a hostile tone. The second speech talks of 'sweet airs', 'delight' and 'riches'. This gives the impression of a pleasant daydream for Caliban.

Section C
Use this work as preparation for your Shakespeare coursework.

ESSAY SPIDERGRAMS

Section A
1 c
2 b
3 c
4 a
5 b

Section B

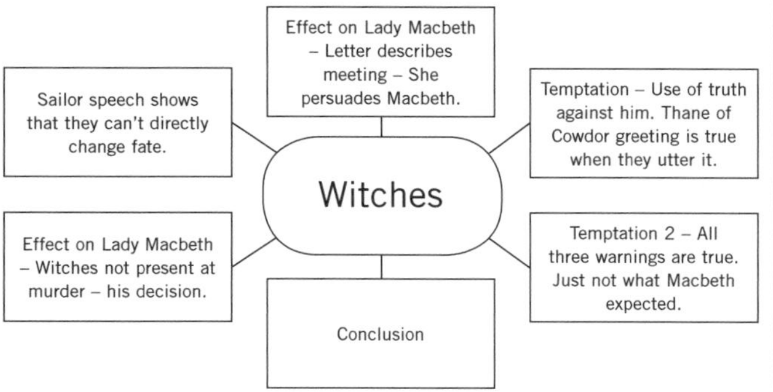

Section C

Give yourself marks out of 10 – 1 for each point made. Have someone check your work.

READING SET POEMS

Section A

1 c
2 d
3 c
4 d
5 a

Section B

1 A sonnet.
2 Jellies implies that his body is soft and squashy: the web of nerves shows that he sees the nerves as holding everything together: the brain image says something about the shape of the brain as in the saying 'use your loaf'; blood as soup implies that the body is nourished by the blood.
3 That the body is a machine.
4 It is surprising that he cares about a machine.
5 The imagery gives a good impression of the different and often conflicting views people have of their own bodies.

Section C

Give yourself 1 mark for each image identified and 1 mark for a comment made on the image.

WRITING ABOUT POETRY (EN2)

Section A

1 b
2 a
3 c
4 d
5 a

Section B

1 To get on or prosper in the world
2 1 Occupation, 2 Art, 3 Science
3 It is used for success in love, not for success in the world
4 The poem is attacking lying and the strong rhyme helps it to make points forcefully – particularly in the last stanza
5 No. The poem is using irony to attack lying

Section C

For practice only

COMPARING POEMS

Section A

1 c
2 d
3 c
4 b
5 a

Section B

1 Loneliness, isolation or arrogance
2 Simple natural imagery
3 An animal in its natural habitat
4 Personification, aaa, bbb rhyme scheme, metaphor or simile

Section C

For practice only

PLANNING A POETRY ESSAY

Section A

1 b
2 d
3 c
4 c
5 a

Section B

Give yourself a mark for each box filled in. You should be able to add at least one point per box. If you cannot do this for a pair of poems you should probably avoid pairing them in the exam.

Section C

Give yourself a mark for each space filled in.

WRITING ON POETIC TECHNIQUE

Section A

1 b
2 a
3 c
4 d
5 b

Section B

1 They are both speaking about love in an exaggerated fashion
2 Donne's poem is about his current love. Marvell's is about an affair he hopes will happen
3 The writer notes a shift of mood in both poems. From angry to calm in Donne and from flattery to threats in Marvell
4 The response could have been improved by either close references to the text or quotations

Section C

1 They are both sonnets (the title of the Shakespeare poem is a big clue)
2 They both have 14 lines
3 Their rhyme schemes
4 Shakespeare's ideas change at lines 9 (But...) and 15 (Therefore...) Rossetti uses an idea throughout
5 Shakespeare's use of a rhyming couplet at the end gives greater impact.

DIFFERENT CULTURAL TEXTS (EN2)

Section A

1 d
2 b
3 c
4 d
5 b

Section B

1 They refer to thirst.
2 They echo the dripping of the water.
3 Blessings, kindly god, roar of tongues, congregation.
4 When you are normally thirsty a sudden rush of water seems like a miracle.
5 It gives a sense of excitement, and also of desperation. The list goes from things designed to hold water through to the only things available.
6 This is a powerful image as it combines both heat and water to make a pleasant and beautiful thing. On its own the sun is a source of discomfort at the beginning of the poem.

Section C

Award marks for points made, backed up with a quotation and comment.

COMPARING CULTURAL TEXTS (EN2)

Section A

1 b
2 a
3 c
4 b
5 d

Section B

1 Use of the word 'lairey' and various non-Standard expressions such as 'just rude' or 'which I hate'.
2 People are less likely to take it seriously as it has a very informal and chatty tone.
3 People judge you according to your accent. Even 'posh' accents can be socially unacceptable in some circumstances.
4 She comments on the thoughtlessness of people who use the word 'half-caste' and she appreciates John Agard's point about the positive nature of mixtures. She even connects Agard's imagery with similar imagery used in a song by Stevie Wonder and Paul McCartney.

Section C

Award marks for points made backed up with a quotation and comment.

NOVELS AND SHORT STORIES

Section A

1 b
2 b
3 b
4 d
5 d

Section B

The Outsider, *The Catcher in the Rye*, *Crime and Punishment*, *Paradise Lost*, *A Christmas Carol*, *Moby Dick*, *Ulysses*, *Don Quixote*, *Alice in Wonderland*

Section C

a) E. M. Forster, *A Room with a View*
b) George Orwell, *1984*
c) Thomas Hardy, *Far from the Madding Crowd*
d) Iain Banks, *The Crow Road*
e) Charles Dickens, *A Tale of Two Cities*
f) Jane Austen, *Pride and Prejudice*
g) H. G. Wells, *The War of the Worlds*
h) Robert Louis Stevenson, *The Strange Case of Dr Jekyll and Mr Hyde*
i) Charlotte Brontë, *Jane Eyre*
j) George Eliot, *Middlemarch*

NOVELS AND SHORT STORIES

Section A

1 b
2 a
3 d
4 c
5 d

Section B

1 Six times.
2 He wishes to give the impression that ALL the items in the list impressed themselves on Pip at once. He got the whole picture, not separate parts.

3 a) It starts off describing what he is like, then it describes things that have happened to him, then it describes how he acts.
   b) The first sentence has no verb at all, as if Magwitch was just there. The first verbs show his adventures, the second set shows his responses. All the things that are happening are unpleasant.
   c) He is clearly a man of action.
4 Magwitch's vocabulary is quite formal but his pronunciation is not. He uses dialect forms like 'them wittles' but he uses rhetorical repetition to emphasise his point about 'that young man'. Magwitch is probably quite intelligent.
5 Magwitch is an escaped criminal. The idea that he is the pirate from the gibbet gives us the impression that his escape will not be for long. The association with death foreshadows Magwitch's eventual fate in the book.

Section C

Your response to this plan can be submitted as coursework.

LITERARY TECHNIQUE (EN2)

Section A

1 b
2 c
3 c
4 a
5 b

Section B

1 It seems to begin with an ending.
2 The focus on death sets up the ghostly part of the story. The slightly humorous tone tells us that it is not to be taken too seriously.
3 Both serious and frivolous.
4 He is 'outside' the story and is prepared to express his own ideas even if they don't move the story on very much. He has a slight sense of humour.
5 It was very bleak. He only had one 'friend' who wasn't even very upset about his death.

Section C

Give yourself a mark out of 20 and have someone check your work. Remove 1 mark for every error made.

THEMES, MOOD, ATMOSPHERE (EN2)

Section A

1 c
2 b
3 c
4 b
5 d

Section B

1 Her hair.
2 His watch.
3 They have each sacrificed something important to themselves to get a gift for the other person. Unfortunately the gifts they have bought relate to the thing sacrificed – the watch chain is useless without the watch and the combs are not necessary for Della's short hair.
4 Sentimental.
5 It is a good ending as there is balance between the two characters.
   It is also an unusual and surprising outcome.

Section C

For practice only.

SHORT STORIES

Section A

1 a
2 c
3 b
4 a
5 b

Section B

1 Optimistic, hopeful
2 The use of the word hope, and the ideas of progress associated with Michael Obi
3 Frustrated
4 The description like 'stifled', 'stuffed' and 'choked'
5 Both use a third person narrative but Achebe is much more distant from the main character. Desai writes more closely from the children's point of view
6 Both openings set up characters and situations

Section C

For practice only.

EXAM TECHNIQUE

Section A

1 b
2 c
3 c
4 a
5 d

Section B

1 Persuasive.
2 Facts – Some people are vegetarians for religious reasons. A kilo of beef costs ten times more than a kilo of wheat to produce. Meat gives an energy return of 34.5 per cent. Plants give an energy return of 328 per cent. Opinions – Most people choose to become vegetarians because of their ideas about animals. Killing animals is unfair. Meat is unacceptably expensive.
3 Some humour and some emotive language.
4 Mostly facts and figures.
5 Capital letters for emphasis in the second paragraph.

Section C

Use the following as a guide:

0–5 Ground covered but not many examples. Little language variety.
6–9 Case well made. Some examples. Use of persuasive language.
10–14 Well written. Persuasive/emotive language. Lively content.
15–18 Very well written and structured. Deliberate and sustained use of language for particular effects.

Answers

ACKNOWLEDGEMENTS

The author and publisher are grateful to the copyright holders for permission to use quoted materials and photographs.

Every effort has been made to trace the copyright holders and to obtain their permission for the use of copyright material. The author and publisher will gladly receive information enabling them to rectify any error or omission in subsequent editions.

Letts and Lonsdale
4 Grosvenor Place
London SW1X 7DL

School orders: 015395 64910
School enquiries: 015395 65921
Parent and student enquiries: 015395 64913
Email: enquiries@lettsandlonsdale.co.uk
Website: www.lettsandlonsdale.com

First published 2007

British Library Cataloguing in Publication Data. A CIP record of this book is available from the British Library.

ISBN: 9781843157946

Book concept and development: Helen Jacobs, Publishing Director

Editorial: Catherine Dakin and Katie Smith

Author: John Mannion

Cover design: Angela English

Inside concept design: Starfish Design

Text design and layout: Ken Vail Graphic Design

Letts and Lonsdale make every effort to ensure t
all paper used in our books is made from wood p
obtained from well-managed forests.

C

This is a coursework practice question. Answer all parts of the question. Continue on separate sheets of paper where necessary.

Writing about plot

Use the following writing frame to discuss the plot of your set play.
There are no marks for this exercise but it could be used as part of your essay preparation.

In .... the most important event as far as plot is concerned is

....

The first consequence of this event is

....

....

A further consequence is

....

....

The main character's response to the event is

....

....

Another character who is affected is

....

....

The language used at this point in the play shows

....

....

Shakespeare structures this part of the play so that

....

....

The effect on the audience of this event is

....

....

Through this event Shakespeare is able to explore the theme of

....

....

Note: You can use this frame as part of a longer essay.

For more on this topic see pages 46–47 of your Success Guide.

Total score / 5

How well did you do?	✗ 0–1 Try again	2–3 Getting there	4 Good work	5 Excellent! ✓

Structure and themes

A

Choose just one answer: a, b, c or d.

1 The theme of a play is:
a) the main idea or message of the play
b) any idea that occurs more than once
c) the main motivation of the characters
d) the reason why the play was written (1 mark)

2 Which of the following plays does not include love as an important theme?
a) *Romeo and Juliet*
b) *Twelfth Night*
c) *Henry V*
d) *The Winter's Tale* (1 mark)

3 The structure of a Shakespeare play is:
a) extremely varied
b) always based on a well-known story
c) what makes it exciting
d) how the plot develops over its five acts (1 mark)

4 The climax of a play:
a) is another name for the ending
b) is the point of highest tension in the play
c) usually involves a murder
d) is the point where we find out most about the main character (1 mark)

5 Shakespeare's comedies often end:
a) in chaos
b) when one of the main characters reveals his or her identity
c) with a marriage
d) with a speech of farewell (1 mark)

Score / 5

B

Answer all parts of all questions.

Most plays by Shakespeare explore more than one theme. Often these will be explored through the actions of particular characters. The themes generally have a message or conclusion.

Fill in the table below with notes on the play you are studying.

Themes	Characters	Conclusion / message
1		
2		
3		

Score / 9

C

These are GCSE-style questions. Answer all parts of the questions.

Writing about structure

The following questions will help you to think about the structure of the play you have studied.

1 How are the main characters introduced?

....

....

(2 marks)

2 What problems or complications occur in the early part of the play?

....

....

(2 marks)

3 Describe how things become chaotic towards the middle of the play.

....

....

....

....

(4 marks)

4 What events bring your play to its climax?

....

....

....

....

(4 marks)

5 How are the problems in the play resolved?

....

....

(2 marks)

Score / 14

For more on this topic see pages 48–49 of your Success Guide.

Total score / 28

How well did you do? ✗ 0–6 Try again 7–14 Getting there 15–22 Good work 23–28 Excellent! ✓

Shakespeare's imagery

A

Choose just one answer: a, b, c or d.

1 **'Feather of lead, bright smoke, cold fire, sick health' (*Romeo and Juliet*) are examples of:**
a) simile
b) metaphor
c) personification
d) oxymoron **(1 mark)**

2 **'Our doubts are traitors' (*Measure for Measure*) is an example of:**
a) a simile
b) a metaphor
c) personification
d) oxymoron **(1 mark)**

3 **'Violent delights have violent ends' (*Romeo and Juliet*) is an example of:**
a) repetition for emphasis
b) repetition for contrast
c) oxymoron
d) symbolism **(1 mark)**

4 **'She sat like Patience on a monument' (*Twelfth Night*) is an example of:**
a) a simile
b) a metaphor
c) personification
d) oxymoron **(1 mark)**

5 **'Time hath, my lord, a wallet at his back, Wherein he puts alms for oblivion' (*Troilus and Cressida*) is an example of:**
a) a simile
b) a metaphor
c) personification
d) oxymoron **(1 mark)**

Score /5

B

Read the following speech from *The Merchant of Venice* and answer the question that follows.

Portia: The quality of mercy is not strain'd;
It droppeth as the gentle rain from heaven
Upon the place beneath. It is twice blest:
It blesseth him that gives and him that takes.
'Tis mightiest in the mightiest; it becomes
The throned monarch better than his crown;
His sceptre shows the force of temporal power,
The attribute to awe and majesty,
Wherein doth sit the dread and fear of kings;
But mercy is above this sceptred sway,
It is enthroned in the hearts of kings,
It is an attribute to God himself;
And earthly power doth then show likest God's

What are the 'qualities of mercy' according to this extended metaphor?

....

....

Score /5

C This is an exam preparation question. Answer all questions.

Writing about imagery – the blood motif in *Macbeth*.
If you are not studying *Macbeth* you can apply this exercise to the play you are studying.
The word 'blood' occurs 41 times in *Macbeth*. In the quotations that follow we can see how Shakespeare exploits this motif as his characters develop during the play.

Macbeth with King Duncan's blood on his hands
ACT 2 SCENE 2
MACBETH:
Whence is that knocking?
How is't with me, when every noise appals me?
What hands are here? Ha, they pluck out mine eyes!
Will all great Neptune's ocean wash this blood
Clean from my hand? No, this my hand will rather
The multitudinous seas incarnadine,
Making the green one red.

Re-enter LADY MACBETH.
LADY MACBETH:
My hands are of your colour, but I shame
To wear a heart so white. …
Retire we to our chamber.
A little water clears us of this deed.
How easy is it then! Your constancy
Hath left you unattended.

Macbeth dismisses his wife's fears
ACT 3 SCENE 4
MACBETH:
I am in blood
Stepp'd in so far that, should I wade no more,
Returning were as tedious as go o'er.

Lady Macbeth is sleep walking and talking to herself
ACT 5 SCENE 1
LADY MACBETH:
Out, damned spot! Out, I say! One – two – why then 'tis time to do't. Hell is murky. Fie, my lord, fie! A soldier, and afeard? What need we fear who knows it, when none can call our power to account? Yet who would have thought the old man to have had so much blood in him?

LADY MACBETH:
Here's the smell of the blood still. All the perfumes of Arabia will not sweeten this little hand. Oh, oh, oh!

1. **Describe Macbeth's reaction to Duncan's blood on his hands.**

   ……………………………………………………
   ……………………………………………………
   ……………………………………………………
   ……………………………………………………

2. **Describe Lady Macbeth's reaction.**

   ……………………………………………………
   ……………………………………………………
   ……………………………………………………
   ……………………………………………………

3. **How does Macbeth feel about blood half way through the play?**

   ……………………………………………………
   ……………………………………………………
   ……………………………………………………
   ……………………………………………………

4. **How has the memory of Duncan's blood affected Lady Macbeth's mental state by the end of the play?**

   ……………………………………………………
   ……………………………………………………
   ……………………………………………………
   ……………………………………………………

5. **How has Shakespeare used imagery to emphasise Lady Macbeth's change of attitude?**

   ……………………………………………………
   ……………………………………………………
   ……………………………………………………
   ……………………………………………………

Score / 10

For more on this topic see pages 50–51 of your Success Guide.

Total score / 20

How well did you do? ✗ 0–4 Try again 5–10 Getting there 11–15 Good work 16–20 Excellent! ✓

An essay on Caliban

A

The following questions relate to *The Tempest*. Choose just one answer: a, b, c or d.

1 Caliban is:
a) a follower of Antonio
b) the only character native to the island
c) the son of Setebos
d) a warlock (1 mark)

2 Caliban's attitude to Prospero is best described as:
a) respectful b) disdainful
c) dismissive d) resentful (1 mark)

3 The thing that Caliban has in common with Miranda is:
a) ignorance of the wider world
b) a love of poetry
c) dislike of Prospero
d) low tolerance for alcohol (1 mark)

4 The thing that Caliban has in common with Antonio is:
a) dislike of the island
b) a capacity for evil
c) respect for Prospero
d) low quality clothing (1 mark)

5 Caliban and Ariel both:
a) like being Prospero's servants
b) like playing tricks
c) want to be free of Prospero
d) prefer to avoid Prospero (1 mark)

Score / 5

B

Read the following speeches from *The Tempest* and then answer the questions that follow.

CALIBAN: All the infections that the sun sucks up
From bogs, fens, flats, on Prosper fall, and make him
By inch-meal a disease! His spirits hear me,
And yet I needs must curse. But they'll nor pinch,
Fright me with urchin-shows, pitch me i' th' mire,
Nor lead me, like a firebrand, in the dark
Out of my way, unless he bid 'em; but
For every trifle are they set upon me;
Sometime like apes that mow and chatter at me,
And after bite me; then like hedgehogs which
Lie tumbling in my barefoot way, and mount
Their pricks at my footfall; sometime am I
All wound with adders, who with cloven tongues
Do hiss me into madness.

CALIBAN: Be not afeard. The isle is full of noises,
Sounds, and sweet airs, that give delight, and hurt not.
Sometimes a thousand twangling instruments
Will hum about mine ears; and sometimes voices,
That, if I then had wak'd after long sleep,
Will make me sleep again; and then, in dreaming,
The clouds methought would open and show riches
Ready to drop upon me, that, when I wak'd,
I cried to dream again.

1 What do these two speeches reveal about Caliban's day-to-day existence on the island?

....

.... (2 marks)

2 How would you describe the mood and tone of the two speeches?

....

.... (4 marks)

3 Show how Shakespeare's choice of words and rhythm affects the mood of the two speeches.

....

.... (4 marks)

Score / 10

This is a coursework practice question.

Writing about character

Discussing any character involves five factors:

- what the character *says*
- what the character *does*
- what the other characters say *to* the character
- what the other characters say *about* the character
- how the character changes or develops

Use these five headings to make notes on Caliban (or any other character you have studied). You may find it easier if you copy it out on to a separate sheet of paper.

There are no marks for this exercise but it could be used as part of your essay preparation.

Caliban				
What he *says*	What he *does*	What the other characters say *to* him	What the other characters say *about* him	How he changes or develops

For more on this topic see pages 52–55 of your Success Guide.

Total score / 15

How well did you do? ✗ 0–3 Try again 4–8 Getting there 9–12 Good work 13–15 Excellent! ✓

Essay spidergrams

A

Choose just one answer: a, b, c or d.

1 Which of the following is not suitable as a subject for a spider diagram?
a) discussing a theme
b) exploring a character
c) telling the story of a play or novel
d) investigating imagery **(1 mark)**

2 Before you begin a spider diagram you should
a) make sure you have suitable pens and paper available
b) check the key words of the question for suitable headings
c) brainstorm ideas
d) sharpen your pencils **(1 mark)**

3 What is the point of colouring-in a completed spider diagram?
a) it looks good
b) the colour makes it easier to remember
c) the different colours are a way of grouping ideas together
d) to make it look like a map of the London Underground **(1 mark)**

4 A spider diagram is a good method of planning because:
a) it helps you see the connections between ideas
b) it makes a memorable revision aid
c) unexpected connections sometimes come up
d) it's a more creative approach than just jotting down points **(1 mark)**

5 If you run out of space on a spider diagram, you should:
a) re-do it using smaller writing
b) add extra paper to keep all your ideas in one place
c) cut out some of the less important ideas
d) re-do it using a bigger sheet of paper **(1 mark)**

Score / 5

B

Study the notes below on *Macbeth* and then complete the task that follows. Write your answer on separate paper.

Question: Are the witches responsible for the tragedy of Macbeth?

Sailor speech shows that they can't directly change fate

Temptation – Use the truth against him. Thane of Cawdor greeting is true when they utter it

Temptation 2 – All three warnings are true. Just not what Macbeth expected

Effect on Macbeth – Witches not present at murder – his decision

Effect on Lady Macbeth – Letter describes meeting – she persuades Macbeth

Conclusion

Rearrange these notes as a spider diagram.

Which version is easier to follow?

Score / 6

This is an exam practice question.

Planning an essay

Use a spider diagram to plan an essay that discusses Shakespeare's presentation of the main character of the play you have studied.

Consider:

- how we are introduced to the character
- how the character changes
- key relationships
- important plot developments

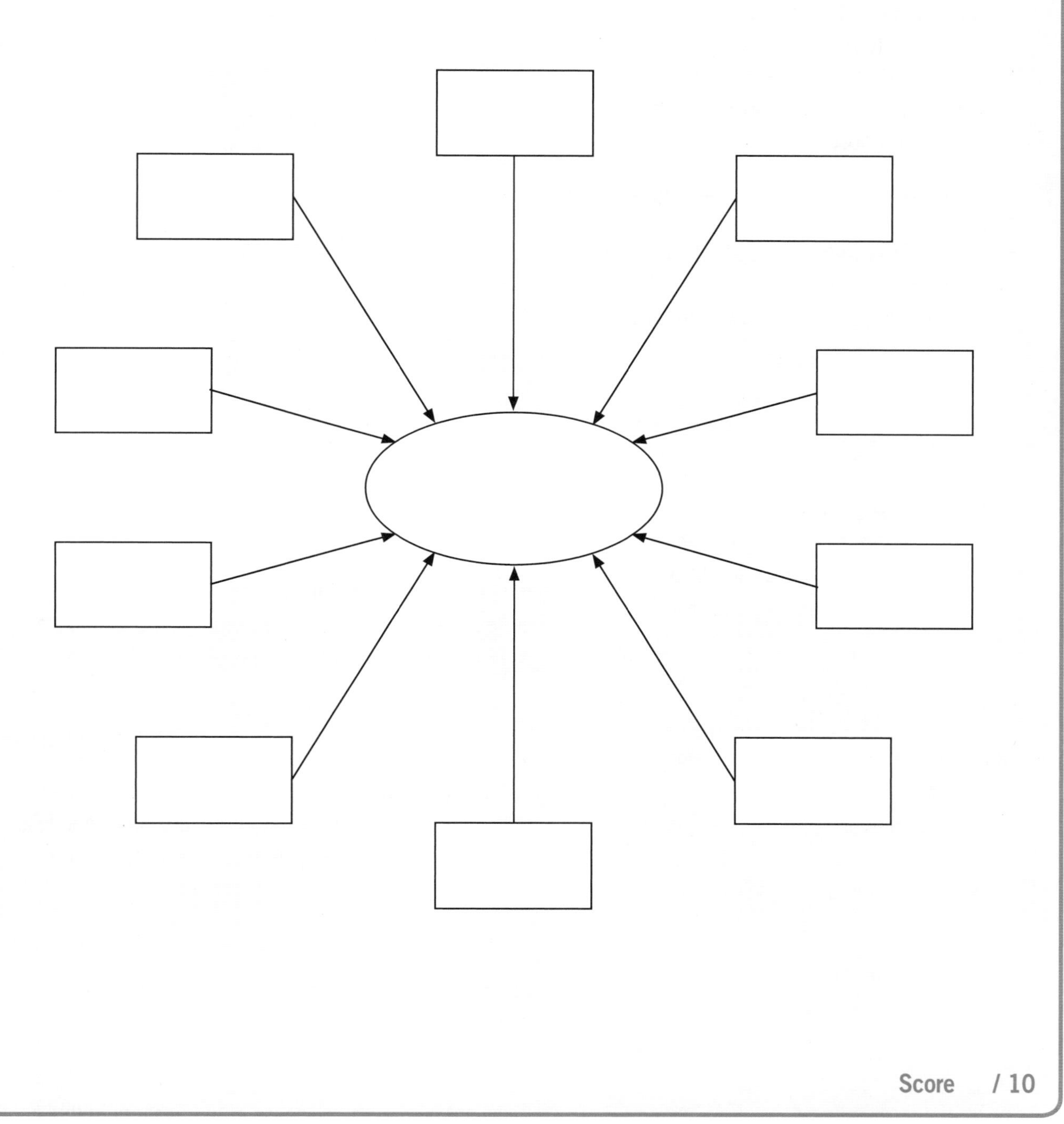

Score / 10

For more on this topic see pages 56–57 of your Success Guide.

Total score / 21

How well did you do? 0–8 Try again 9–12 Getting there 13–18 Good work 19–21 Excellent!

Reading set poems

A

Choose just one answer: a, b, c or d.

1 Poetry is studied:
a) as part of English only
b) as part of English literature only
c) as part of English and English literature
d) via unseen tests **(1 mark)**

2 A poem's tone is determined by:
a) the attitude it expresses
b) its theme
c) the choice of poetic form
d) all of the above **(1 mark)**

3 You can get high marks when studying poetry if you:
a) identify the figures of speech the poet has used
b) identify the verse form and genre of the poem
c) identify and explain the figures of speech in the poem
d) do all of the above **(1 mark)**

4 Which of the following is not a figure of speech?
a) simile
b) metaphor
c) metonym
d) diction **(1 mark)**

5 A metaphor states that:
a) one thing is another
b) one thing is like another
c) one thing resembles another
d) two things resemble each other **(1 mark)**

Score /5

B

Read the following short poem using the advice on pages 60–61 of your Success Guide.

I've made out a will; I'm leaving myself
to the National Health. I'm sure they can use
the jellies and tubes and syrups and glues,
the web of nerves and veins, the loaf of brains,

and assortment of fillings and stitches and wounds,
blood – a gallon exactly of bilberry soup –
the chassis or cage or cathedral of bone;
but not the heart, they can leave that alone.
They can have the lot, the whole stock:
the loops and coils and sprockets and springs
and rods
the twines and cords and strands
the face, the case, the cogs and the hands,

but not the pendulum, the ticker;
leave that where it stops or hangs.

Simon Armitage

1 What kind of poem is this?

.... **(1 mark)**

2 In the first half of the poem, the speaker uses a series of images for his body. Choose two and explain what attitude this choice of image communicates.

....

.... **(4 marks)**

3 The second half of the poem uses a single extended metaphor for the body. What is this metaphor and what does it reveal about the speaker's view of his body?

....

.... **(3 marks)**

4 Given the attitude expressed in the second half of the poem, why is the final line surprising?

.... **(1 mark)**

5 Comment on the effectiveness of the imagery in this poem.

.... **(2 marks)**

Score /11

This is a GCSE-style question. Plan your answer here and write your response on separate paper.

Choose one other poem that you have studied that makes interesting use of imagery.

Compare it with *I've made out a will; I'm leaving myself.*

Write about:

- the images used in the two poems
- the similarities and differences between them
- which poem you found most effective

Remember to support your comments with quotations.

Score / 12

For more on this topic see pages 60–61 of your Success Guide.

Total score / 28

How well did you do? ✗ 0–6 Try again 7–14 Getting there 15–22 Good work 23–28 Excellent! ✓

Writing about poetry (EN2)

A

Choose just one answer: a, b, c or d.

1 The theme of a poem is:
a) a recurring phrase or set of lines
b) its central message or idea
c) the general atmosphere it creates
d) the poet's intention (1 mark)

2 Assonance occurs in a line of poetry when:
a) the same vowel sound is used with different consonants
b) the same sound is used at the beginning of every word
c) a deliberately jarring note is introduced
d) there is a change in the rhythm of the line (1 mark)

3 A caesura is:
a) the same sound used at the beginning of a series of words
b) when the meaning runs over from one line to another
c) a pause in the middle of a line
d) a word that makes the sound it describes (1 mark)

4 A quatrain is another name for:
a) a rapid flowing rhythm
b) the first part of a poem
c) a repeated phrase or line
d) a four line stanza (1 mark)

5 Onomatopoeia occurs when:
a) the words of a poem make the same sound as the one being described
b) the rhythm of the poem resembles the rhythm being described
c) the poem contains words that mimic the sound they describe
d) all of the above (1 mark)

Score /5

B

Read the following poem and then answer the questions that follow.

A Song

Lying is an occupation
used by all who mean to rise:
Politicians owe their station
But to well-concerted lies.

These to lovers give assistance
To ensnare the fair one's heart;
And the virgin's best resistance
Yields to this commanding art.

Study this superior science,
Would you rise in church or state;
Bid to truth a bold defiance,
`Tis the practise of the great.

Laetitia Pilkington (1708–50)

1 Explain what is meant by the word 'rise' as used in the first and third stanzas.

....

.... (2 marks)

2 The skill of lying is described in a different way in each stanza. What are the three different ways?

....

.... (3 marks)

3 What is different about the use of lying in the second stanza?

....

.... (2 marks)

4 Why do you think this poem has a strong and simple rhyme scheme?

....

.... (2 marks)

5 Do you think that the advice given in the poem is meant to be taken seriously? Give a reason for your answer.

....

.... (3 marks)

Score /12

C This is a GCSE-style question. Answer all parts of the question.

Use the following writing frame to explore *Song.*

The main theme of this poem is

....

However, rather than attacking its theme directly the poet uses irony

....

This can be seen when she says

....

Another example is

....

The poem's use of language is

....

A good example of this is when

....

By using language in this way the poet makes her message

....

The imagery used in the poem is

....

For example

....

The middle stanza is slightly different because it refers to

....

However, all the stanzas attack men

....

The strong and simple rhyme scheme works well because

....

The best example is

....

The tone/mood of the poem is

....

This is most noticeable

....

In my view this poem works well because

....

I particularly liked

....

This kind of writing frame can be used in your study of an individual poem before you go on to make a comparison.

For more on this topic see pages 62–63 of your Success Guide.

Total score / 17

How well did you do? 0–3 Try again 4–9 Getting there 10–13 Good work 14–17 Excellent!

Comparing poems

A

Choose just one answer: a, b, c or d.

1 Which of the following themes is not a feature of Seamus Heaney's poetry?
a) nature
b) autobiography
c) exploring characters from fiction or history
d) adult – child relationships **(1 mark)**

2 When studying poems by the same author you should look for:
a) consistent themes
b) typical subject matter
c) favourite poetic techniques
d) all of the above **(1 mark)**

3 Which of the following is not a way of grouping poems for comparison?
a) author b) theme
c) title d) poetic technique **(1 mark)**

4 When choosing poems to compare you should make sure:
a) they have a similar length
b) they have similar themes
c) they have similar titles
d) they have similar authors **(1 mark)**

5 If you are writing about a poem in an exam you should:
a) write notes on the printed poem
b) not write notes on the printed poem
c) avoid cluttering your poem with too many notes
d) first try to remember notes you previously made **(1 mark)**

Score /5

B

Read the poem below and then answer the questions.

The Eagle

He clasps the crag
with crooked hands;
Close to the sun in
lonely lands,
Ringed with the azure
world, he stands.
The wrinkled sea
beneath him crawls;
He watches from his
mountain walls,
And like a thunderbolt
he falls.

Alfred, Lord Tennyson

1 What is the theme of this poem?
.... **(1 mark)**
Write down the name of a poem you have studied on a similar theme.
....

2 What is interesting about the imagery of this poem?
.... **(1 mark)**
Write down the name of a poem you have studied that has similar imagery. ....

3 What is this poem about?
.... **(1 mark)**
Write down the name of a poem you have studied that has similar subject matter. ....

4 What poetic techniques does this poem use?
.... **(2 marks)**
Write down the name of a poem you have studied that uses similar techniques. ....

Score /5

This is a GCSE-style question.

Comparing poems

Using *The Eagle* and one of the poems you named in section B fill in the following grid.

	Subject matter	Theme	Words and imagery	Poetic technques
The Eagle				
Poem 2				
Similarities and differences				

For more on this topic see pages 64–67 of your Success Guide.

Total score / 10

How well did you do? 0–2 Try again 3–5 Getting there 6–8 Good work 9–10 Excellent!

Planning a poetry essay

A

Choose just one answer: a, b, c or d.

1 In a poetry essay you should usually plan to write about:

a) one poem only
b) two or three poems
c) as many poems as you can remember
d) all the poems in your anthology **(1 mark)**

2 When comparing and contrasting poems you should:

a) write about one poem at a time and contrast them at the end
b) write comparisons after each section of the answer
c) compare freely as you go along
d) do any of the above **(1 mark)**

3 Which of the following is not a good approach to essay writing:

a) using a spider diagram
b) compiling a comparison table
c) planning as you write to allow maximum time
d) annotation of the text of the poems **(1 mark)**

4 Many questions name one poem and allow you to pick a second one. You should choose:

a) the poem you know most about
b) the poem the examiners seem to expect
c) the poem that has the most similarities and differences that you can discuss
d) any poem that you have really enjoyed **(1 mark)**

5 PEC stands for:

a) Point, Example, Comment
b) Point, Example, Comparison
c) Point, Examine, Contrast
d) Pair, Examine, Compare **(1 mark)**

Score / 5

B

Use the grid below to plan a comparison between two poems that you have studied.

	Common theme	How the poems differ	How the theme is expressed	Words and images	Poetic techniques (verse form, rhyme, etc.)
Poem A					
Poem B					

Score / 10

C

This is a GCSE-style question.
Either fill in the spaces below or use a separate piece of paper and use the text given to structure your answer.

Comparing poems

Choose two poems that you have studied that have given an insight into the author's life and times.

The two poems I have chosen are .... and .... Each poem gives me an insight into its author's life and times but the first poem is about .... and the second poem is about ....

The main thing that the two poems have in common is .... We can see this when the first poem says .... (quotation). In the second poem we can see this when it says .... (quotation). Both/neither poem .... (comment).

However, the two poems have very different views about .... The first poem shows this in the words .... (quotation) whereas the second poem says .... (quotation). The contrast between the two poems shows .... (comment).

The words in which the poets express their ideas show some interesting similarities. The first poem uses .... (quotation) and .... (quotation). In the second poem the poet says .... (quotation) and .... (quotation). This shows us that .... (comment). In contrast, the first poem says .... (quotation) and .... (quotation). The difference in language choice indicates .... (comment)

The two poets' use of poetic technique is very similar/different. For instance, the first poem uses .... (example) and .... (example). The second poem uses .... (example) and .... (example). The similarities/differences we can see are probably because .... (comment) or .... (comment).

The two poems use similar/different poetic forms. The first poem uses .... and .... whilst the second one uses .... and .... The use of these forms tells us .... (comment)

In conclusion

....

....

....

....

(comment)

Score /31

For more on this topic see pages 66–67 of your Success Guide.

Total score /46

How well did you do? 0–10 Try again 11–23 Getting there 24–36 Good work 37–46 Excellent!

Writing on poetic technique

A

Choose just one answer: a, b, c or d.

1 Poems written before 1914:
a) are always written in blank verse
b) tend to be more formal in their use of poetic techniques
c) can be more difficult to understand than modern poems
d) need to be studied more carefully than modern poems (1 mark)

2 An example of a poetic form is:
a) sonnet b) metaphor
c) personification d) rhyme scheme (1 mark)

3 When choosing poems to compare you should:
a) pick the poems you know best
b) choose poems that have a similar structure
c) choose poems that have strong similarities or areas of contrast
d) try to guess which poems the examiners had in mind (1 mark)

4 Which of the following is an example of nature imagery?
a) Let me not to the marriage of true minds admit impediment
b) I have measured out my life in coffee spoons
c) Stop all the clocks
d) The sea is calm tonight (1 mark)

5 A dramatic monologue is:
a) an extract from a play
b) a poem spoken by a character who is not the poet
c) a poem containing only one voice
d) a poem written in quatrains (1 mark)

Score / 5

B

Below is a short passage from a student's response to two poems on the theme of men and women. Read the passage and then answer the questions.

'The Sun Rising' by John Donne and 'To His Coy Mistress' by Andrew Marvell are both poems that speak about love in a very exaggerated fashion. The main difference between the two poems is that Donne is talking about a love affair that is already taking place and Marvell is trying to persuade his lover to go to bed with him. Both poets seem to think spending time with your lover is extremely important; in 'The Sun Rising' Donne is angry with the sun at first because its rising means that their night of passion is over, whereas in 'To His Coy Mistress' the desperate lover says that he is prepared to spend thousands of years simply looking at his mistress. Another feature that the poems have in common is a change in mood. John Donne eventually invites the sun to stay with him and his lover whereas Andrew Marvell moves from extravagant praise to sinister threats in the second part of the poem.

1 What is the main way in which the two poems are linked?

.... (2 marks)

2 In what way are the two poems contrasted?

.... (2 marks)

3 How does the writer compare the moods of the two poems?

.... (2 marks)

4 Can you suggest any improvements to this discussion?

.... (2 marks)

Score / 8

This is a GCSE-style question. Answer all the questions.
Continue on separate sheets of paper where necessary.

Writing about form

Sonnet 138	**How do I love thee?**
When my love swears that she is made of truth I do believe her, though I know she lies, That she might think me some untutor'd youth, Unlearned in the world's false subtleties. Thus vainly thinking that she thinks me young, Although she knows my days are past the best, Simply I credit her false speaking tongue: On both sides thus is simple truth suppress'd. But wherefore says she not she is unjust? And wherefore say not I that I am old? O, love's best habit is in seeming trust, And age in love loves not to have years told: Therefore I lie with her and she with me, And in our faults by lies we flatter'd be.	How do I love thee? Let me count the ways. I love thee to the depth and breadth and height My soul can reach, when feeling out of sight For the ends of Being and ideal Grace. I love thee to the level of everyday's Most quiet need, by sun and candle-light. I love thee freely, as men strive for Right; I love thee purely, as they turn from Praise. I love thee with a passion put to use In my old griefs, and with my childhood's faith. I love thee with a love I seemed to lose With my lost saints, --- I love thee with the breath, Smiles, tears, of all my life! --- and, if God choose, I shall but love thee better after death.
William Shakespeare	**Christina Rossetti**

1 **What form do these two poems have in common?**

....

....

(1 mark)

2 **How can you tell?**

....

....

(1 mark)

3 **What is the main formal difference between them?**

....

....

(2 marks)

4 **How do the two poets divide up their ideas?**

....

....

(4 marks)

5 **Which of the two forms do you think has more impact at the end?**

....

....

(2 marks)

Score / 10

For more on this topic see pages 68–69 of your Success Guide.

Total score / 23

How well did you do? ✗ 0–5 Try again 6–12 Getting there 13–18 Good work 19–23 Excellent! ✓

Different cultural texts (EN2)

A

Choose just one answer: a, b, c or d.

1 Which of the following ideas is unlikely to be explored in your work on texts from different cultures?

a) ideas about language, power and dialect
b) feelings about being caught between two cultures
c) belief and ritual
d) a touristic view of 'abroad' **(1 mark)**

2 Rituals:

a) only take place in churches
b) are a codified way of dealing with common situations
c) are an old-fashioned way of doing something
d) are an interesting pastime **(1 mark)**

3 Enjambment is:

a) a pause in a line of poetry
b) a type of rhythm
c) when the meaning of one line flows onto the next
d) a sort of improvised poetry session **(1 mark)**

4 An elegy is:

a) an eight-line poem
b) a sad poem
c) a type of ballad
d) a poem in praise of a dead person **(1 mark)**

5 Free verse uses:

a) rhyme
b) unrhymed lines of irregular length
c) regular stanzas but no rhyme
d) irregular lines with a set rhyme scheme **(1 mark)**

Score /5

B

Read Imtiaz Dharker's poem *Blessing* and answer the questions below.

Blessing

The skin cracks like a pod.
There never is enough water.
Imagine the drip of it,
the small splash, echo
in a tin mug,
the voice of a kindly god.
Sometimes, the sudden rush
of fortune. The municipal pipe bursts,
silver crashes to the ground
and the flow has found
a roar of tongues. From the huts,
a congregation: every man woman
child for streets around
butts in, with pots,
brass, copper, aluminium,
plastic buckets,
frantic hands,
and naked children
screaming in the liquid sun,
their highlights polished to perfection,
flashing light,
as the blessing sings
over their small bones.

Imtiaz Dharker

1 How are the first two lines different from the rest of the poem?

....

.... **(1 mark)**

2 Why do you think there are so many single syllable words in lines three to five?

....

.... **(2 marks)**

3 There are several religious images in this poem. Can you find three of them?

....

.... **(3 marks)**

4 Why do you think they are used?

....

.... **(2 marks)**

5 What is the purpose of the long list of utensils? How is the list organised?

....

.... **(2 marks)**

6 Comment on the effectiveness of the phrase 'liquid sun'.

....

.... **(2 marks)**

Score /12

This is a GCSE-style question. Plan your answer here and write your response on separate paper.

Comparing texts

Choose one other poem that you have studied that gives you insight into life outside England. Compare it with *Blessing*.

You should write about:

- what you learn about the other country
- the attitude of the poet
- the way in which the two poets have expressed their ideas.

Refer back to the framework on page 63 of your Success Guide to help you structure your answer.

Score / 20

For more on this topic see pages 70–71 of your Success Guide.

Total score / 37

How well did you do? 0–7 Try again 8–19 Getting there 20–28 Good work 29–37 Excellent!

Comparing cultural texts (EN2)

A

Choose just one answer: a, b, c or d.

1 Received Pronunciation or BBC English is:
a) the way language is spoken by most people in England
b) the way that many powerful and influential people speak
c) another way of saying 'the Queen's English'
d) a way of speaking that has to be learned – it is not natural (1 mark)

2 A dialect is:
a) a version of English with its own rules, vocabulary and grammar
b) a version of English that has mistakes in it
c) any version of English that is not spoken with a BBC accent
d) a lower status version of English (1 mark)

3 Which one of the following statements about accent is correct?
a) it is impossible to speak Standard English if you have a regional accent
b) accent is the same as dialect
c) accent describes the way Standard English is spoken in a particular area
d) people with posh accents always speak Standard English (1 mark)

4 Phonetic spelling is:
a) a special way of writing used by children learning to read
b) an attempt to write words down as they sound, not as they are spelt in a dictionary
c) deliberately distorted spelling used by poets for effect
d) an ancient writing system used by the Phoenicians (1 mark)

5 Irony is:
a) a way of expressing anger
b) harsh and unpleasant speech
c) the name of one of the dialects of English
d) the device of saying one thing and meaning another (1 mark)

Score /5

B

Read the following extract from a student's comparison of *Unrelated incidents* and *Half-caste*, and then complete the questions that follow.

I didn't find either of these poems easy to understand at first as I couldn't work out what they were saying. But when we read them aloud in class it was easier to see what the poets were getting at. I liked half-caste best because it was quite funny but unrelated incidents was just rude. When I thought about it though I realised that Tom Leonard had a point: people are always making fun of other people's accents and being lairey if you don't have a posh one. But I saw the other day that even posh people are trying to get rid of their accents. Half-caste is really about racism – I don't agree with racism and I think it's a good poem because it shows that people don't think about what they're saying half the time.
I also liked the way John Agard showed that mixing things up is a good thing. Unfortunately it reminded me of that song ebony and ivory which I hate.

1 What evidence does this text show that the writer probably doesn't speak BBC English?

....

.... (2 marks)

2 How does the fact that this text is expressed in a non-Standard way affect people's opinions?

....

.... (2 marks)

3 What comment does she make about social attitudes to accent?

....

.... (2 marks)

4 What two good points does the text make about *Half-Caste*?

....

.... (2 marks)

Score /8

This is a GCSE-style question. Plan your answer here and write your response on separate paper.

Comparing poems

Choose either *Half-Caste* or *Unrelated Incidents* and then compare your choice with another poem you have studied.

You should write about:

- what each poet has to say about language
- how language affects the speaker's attitude to life
- the way in which the two poets have expressed their ideas

Refer back to the framework on page 63 of your Success Guide to help you structure your answer.

Score / 20

For more on this topic see pages 72–73 of your Success Guide.

Total score / 33

How well did you do? ✗ 0–7 Try again 8–17 Getting there 18–25 Good work 26–33 Excellent! ✓

Novels and short stories

A

Choose just one answer: a, b, c or d.

1 In which exam is your knowledge of your set text tested?
a) English
b) English Literature
c) both – it is a 'crossover' unit
d) neither – it is a coursework unit **(1 mark)**

2 Which of the following texts would *not* be suitable for an English and English literature prose study unit?
a) *Great Expectations* by Charles Dickens
b) *Harry Potter and the Chamber of Secrets* by J.K. Rowling
c) *Silas Marner* by George Eliot
d) *Treasure Island* by Robert Louis Stevenson **(1 mark)**

3 A collection of short stories can be studied if they are:
a) about as difficult as a novel
b) about the same theme
c) about the same characters
d) set in the same place **(1 mark)**

4 H. G. Wells is most famous for writing:
a) detective stories
b) historical stories
c) romances
d) science fiction stories **(1 mark)**

5 How much writing is required for a prose study?
a) 500 words
b) 750 words
c) 1000 words
d) none at all if you are assessed orally **(1 mark)**

Score / 5

B

Answer all parts of the question below.

Which of the following authors and titles are not suitable for an English and English Literature crossover prose study?

Circle those that apply.

a) *The Outsider* (Novel) – Albert Camus. French. Post-1914
b) *The Catcher in the Rye* (Novel) – J D Salinger. American. Post-1914
c) *Crime and Punishment* (Novel) – Fyodor Dostoyevski. Russian. Pre-1914
d) *Paradise Lost* (Poem) – John Milton. English. Pre-1914
e) *A Christmas Carol* (Novella) – Charles Dickens. English. Pre-1914
f) *Moby Dick* (Novel) – Herman Melville. American. Pre-1914
g) *Pride and Prejudice* (Novel) – Jane Austen. English. Pre-1914
h) *Ulysses* (Novel) – James Joyce. English. Post-1914
i) *Don Quixote* (Novel) – Miguel de Cervantes. Spanish. Pre-1914
j) *Alice in Wonderland* (Children's story) – Lewis Carroll. English. Pre-1914

Score / 10

C

This is an exam preparation question.

If you have a choice of novel for your prose study you might like to consider one of the novels below. Score one mark if you know the title and one if you know the author of each of the openings below.

Openings of famous novels:

a) 'The Signora had no business to do it', said Miss Bartlett, 'no business at all. She promised us south rooms with a view close together, instead of which, here are north rooms looking into a courtyard, and a long way apart. Oh, Lucy!'

b) It was a bright cold day in April, and the clocks were striking thirteen.

c) When Farmer Oak smiled, the corners of his mouth spread till they were within an unimportant distance of his ears, his eyes were reduced to chinks, and diverging wrinkles appeared round them, extending upon his countenance like the rays in a rudimentary sketch of the rising sun.

d) It was the day my grandmother exploded.

e) It was the best of times, it was the worst of times, it was the age of wisdom, it was the age of foolishness, it was the epoch of belief, it was the epoch of incredulity, it was the season of Light, it was the season of Darkness, it was the spring of hope, it was the winter of despair, we had everything before us, we had nothing before us, we were all going direct to Heaven, we were all going direct the other way—in short, the period was so.

f) It is a truth universally acknowledged, that a single man in possession of a good fortune, must be in want of a wife.

g) No one would have believed in the last years of the nineteenth century that this world was being watched keenly and closely by intelligences greater than man's and yet as mortal as his own; that as men busied themselves about their various concerns they were scrutinised and studied, perhaps almost as narrowly as a man with a microscope might scrutinise the transient creatures that swarm and multiply in a drop of water.

h) Mr. Utterson the lawyer was a man of a rugged countenance, that was never lighted by a smile; cold, scanty and embarrassed in discourse; backward in sentiment; lean, long, dusty, dreary and yet somehow lovable.

i) There was no possibility of taking a walk that day.

j) Miss Brooke had that kind of beauty which seems to be thrown into relief by poor dress.

Score / 20

For more on this topic see pages 76–77 of your Success Guide.

Total score / 35

How well did you do? ✗ 0–7 Try again 8–18 Getting there 19–27 Good work 28–35 Excellent! ✓

Novels and short stories

A

Read the following extract that consists of the whole of Chapter 1 from *Great Expectations* by Charles Dickens.

My father's family name being Pirrip, and my Christian name Philip, my infant tongue could make of both names nothing longer or more explicit than Pip. So, I called myself Pip, and came to be called Pip.

I give Pirrip as my father's family name, on the authority of his tombstone and my sister – Mrs Joe Gargery, who married the blacksmith. As I never saw my father or my mother, and never saw any likeness of either of them (for their days were long before the days of photographs), my first fancies regarding what they were like, were unreasonably derived from their tombstones. The shape of the letters on my father's, gave me an odd idea that he was a square, stout, dark man, with curly black hair. From the character and turn of the inscription, 'Also Georgiana Wife of the Above,' I drew a childish conclusion that my mother was freckled and sickly. To five little stone lozenges, each about a foot and a half long, which were arranged in a neat row beside their grave, and were sacred to the memory of five little brothers of mine – who gave up trying to get a living, exceedingly early in that universal struggle – I am indebted for a belief I religiously entertained that they had all been born on their backs with their hands in their trousers-pockets, and had never taken them out in this state of existence.

Ours was the marsh country, down by the river, within, as the river wound, twenty miles of the sea. My first most vivid and broad impression of the identity of things, seems to me to have been gained on a memorable raw afternoon towards evening. At such a time I found out for certain, that this bleak place overgrown with nettles was the churchyard; and that Philip Pirrip, late of this parish, and also Georgiana wife of the above, were dead and buried; and that Alexander, Bartholomew, Abraham, Tobias, and Roger, infant children of the aforesaid, were also dead and buried; and that the dark flat wilderness beyond the churchyard, intersected with dykes and mounds and gates, with scattered cattle feeding on it, was the marshes; and that the low leaden line beyond, was the river; and that the distant savage lair from which the wind was rushing, was the sea; and that the small bundle of shivers growing afraid of it all and beginning to cry, was Pip.

"Hold your noise!" cried a terrible voice, as a man started up from among the graves at the side of the church porch.

"Keep still, you little devil, or I'll cut your throat!"

A fearful man, all in coarse grey, with a great iron on his leg. A man with no hat, and with broken shoes, and with an old rag tied round his head. A man who had been soaked in water, and smothered in mud, and lamed by stones, and cut by flints, and stung by nettles, and torn by briars; who limped, and shivered, and glared and growled; and whose teeth chattered in his head as he seized me by the chin.

"O! Don't cut my throat, sir," I pleaded in terror. "Pray don't do it, sir."

"Tell us your name!" said the man. "Quick!"

"Pip, sir."

"Once more," said the man, staring at me. "Give it mouth!"

"Pip. Pip, sir."

"Show us where you live," said the man. "Pint out the place!"

I pointed to where our village lay, on the flat in-shore among the alder-trees and pollards, a mile or more from the church.

The man, after looking at me for a moment, turned me upside down, and emptied my pockets. There was nothing in them but a piece of bread. When the church came to itself – for he was so sudden and strong that he made it go head over heels before me, and I saw the steeple under my feet – when the church came to itself, I say, I was seated on a high tombstone, trembling, while he ate the bread ravenously.

"You young dog," said the man, licking his lips, "what fat cheeks you ha' got."

I believe they were fat, though I was at that time undersized for my years, and not strong.

"Darn me if I couldn't eat em," said the man, with a threatening shake of his head, "and if I han't half a mind to't!"

I earnestly expressed my hope that he wouldn't, and held tighter to the tombstone on which he had put me; partly, to keep myself upon it; partly, to keep myself from crying.

"Now lookee here!" said the man. "Where's your mother?"

"There, sir!" said I.

He started, made a short run, and stopped and looked over his shoulder.

"There, sir!" I timidly explained. "Also Georgiana. That's my mother."

"Oh!" said he, coming back. "And is that your father alonger your mother?"

"Yes, sir," said I; "him too; late of this parish."

"Ha!" he muttered then, considering. "Who d'ye live with – supposin' you're kindly let to live, which I han't made up my mind about?"

"My sister, sir – Mrs. Joe Gargery – wife of Joe Gargery, the blacksmith, sir."

"Blacksmith, eh?" said he. And looked down at his leg.

After darkly looking at his leg and me several times, he came closer to my tombstone, took me by both arms, and tilted me back as far as he could hold me; so that his eyes looked most powerfully down into mine, and mine looked most helplessly up into his.

"Now lookee here," he said, "the question being whether you're to be let to live. You know what a file is?"
"Yes, sir."
"And you know what wittles is?"
"Yes, sir."

After each question he tilted me over a little more, so as to give me a greater sense of helplessness and danger.

"You get me a file." He tilted me again. "And you get me wittles." He tilted me again. "You bring 'em both to me." He tilted me again. "Or I'll have your heart and liver out." He tilted me again.

I was dreadfully frightened, and so giddy that I clung to him with both hands, and said, "If you would kindly please to let me keep upright, sir, perhaps I shouldn't be sick, and perhaps I could attend more."

He gave me a most tremendous dip and roll, so that the church jumped over its own weather-cock. Then, he held me by the arms, in an upright position on the top of the stone, and went on in these fearful terms:

"You bring me, to-morrow morning early, that file and them wittles. You bring the lot to me, at that old Battery over yonder. You do it, and you never dare to say a word or dare to make a sign concerning your having seen such a person as me, or any person sumever, and you shall be let to live. You fail, or you go from my words in any partickler, no matter how small it is, and your heart and your liver shall be tore out, roasted and ate. Now, I ain't alone, as you may think I am. There's a young man hid with me, in comparison with which young man I am a Angel. That young man hears the words I speak. That young man has a secret way pecooliar to himself, of getting at a boy, and at his heart, and at his liver. It is in wain for a boy to attempt to hide himself from that young man. A boy may lock his door, may be warm in bed, may tuck himself up, may draw the clothes over his head, may think himself comfortable and safe, but that young man will softly creep and creep his way to him and tear him open. I am a-keeping that young man from harming of you at the present moment, with great difficulty. I find it wery hard to hold that young man off of your inside. Now, what do you say?"

I said that I would get him the file, and I would get him what broken bits of food I could, and I would come to him at the Battery, early in the morning.

"Say Lord strike you dead if you don't!" said the man.

I said so, and he took me down.

"Now," he pursued, "you remember what you've undertook, and you remember that young man, and you get home!"
"Goo-good night, sir," I faltered.
"Much of that!" said he, glancing about him over the cold wet flat. "I wish I was a frog. Or a eel!"

At the same time, he hugged his shuddering body in both his arms – clasping himself, as if to hold himself together – and limped towards the low church wall. As I saw him go, picking his way among the nettles, and among the brambles that bound the green mounds, he looked in my young eyes as if he were eluding the hands of the dead people, stretching up cautiously out of their graves, to get a twist upon his ankle and pull him in.

When he came to the low church wall, he got over it, like a man whose legs were numbed and stiff, and then turned round to look for me. When I saw him turning, I set my face towards home, and made the best use of my legs. But presently I looked over my shoulder, and saw him going on again towards the river, still hugging himself in both arms, and picking his way with his sore feet among the great stones dropped into the marshes here and there, for stepping-places when the rains were heavy, or the tide was in.

The marshes were just a long black horizontal line then, as I stopped to look after him; and the river was just another horizontal line, not nearly so broad nor yet so black; and the sky was just a row of long angry red lines and dense black lines intermixed. On the edge of the river I could faintly make out the only two black things in all the prospect that seemed to be standing upright; one of these was the beacon by which the sailors steered – like an unhooped cask upon a pole – an ugly thing when you were near it; the other a gibbet, with some chains hanging to it which had once held a pirate. The man was limping on towards this latter, as if he were the pirate come to life, and come down, and going back to hook himself up again. It gave me a terrible turn when I thought so; and as I saw the cattle lifting their heads to gaze after him, I wondered whether they thought so too. I looked all round for the horrible young man, and could see no signs of him. But, now I was frightened again, and ran home without stopping.

Glossary: wittles – food. A dialect of slang form of victuals.

gibbet – a wooden structure from which executed bodies were hung.

Novels and short stories

A

Choose just one answer: a, b, c or d.

1 Pip's full name is:
a) Pip Philips
b) Philip Pirrip
c) Pirrip Philips
d) Pip Pirrip (1 mark)

2 How would you describe the atmosphere created in the second and third paragraphs?
a) bleak and cheerless
b) harsh and aggressive
c) sad and mournful
d) flat and monotonous (1 mark)

3 What is noticeable about the way the two characters speak in this extract?
a) Pip and Magwitch both speak in dialect
b) Pip speaks in dialect while Magwitch speaks in Standard English
c) Pip and Magwitch both speak in Standard English
d) Magwitch speaks in dialect while Pip speaks in Standard English (1 mark)

4 What does Magwitch's behaviour suggest?
a) that he is extremely cruel
b) that he is afraid of his friend
c) that he is starving
d) that he likes scaring people (1 mark)

5 What is the purpose of the dialogue in this chapter?
a) to make the story telling vivid and realistic
b) to demonstrate the power relationships between the two characters
c) to show Magwitch's intelligence but lack of education
d) all of the above (1 mark)

Score / 5

B

Answer the following questions based on the passage.

1 In paragraph three, that starts 'Ours was the marsh country …', how many times does Dickens use the phrase 'and that'?

....

.... (1 mark)

2 Why do you think Dickens used this long list instead of placing the information in separate sentences?

....

.... (2 marks)

3 In paragraph five Dickens uses another long list to describe Magwitch.
a) How does the list change as it progresses?

....

.... (2 marks)

b) Why do you think there are so many verbs in the latter part of the list?

....

.... (2 marks)

c) How do all these verbs affect our impression of Magwitch?

....

.... (1 mark)

4 Identify formal and informal features of Magwitch's speech beginning 'You bring me, to-morrow morning early …' What does the speech tell us about Magwitch's intelligence?

....

.... (4 marks)

5 In the final paragraph Magwitch is associated with a corpse coming temporarily back to life. What does this add to our impression of him at this point?

....

.... (2 marks)

Score / 14

This is a coursework practice question.

Coursework: Explore Chapter One as an introduction to *Great Expectations.*

You can use the following essay plan to help you to submit a piece of coursework on *Great Expectations* or you can study the plan to help you with work on a different novel.

Essay plan:

You should write at least a paragraph on each of the following issues:

Setting and atmosphere

- Select elements of the setting and explain the atmosphere and mood created. Make sure you mention the types of images used (if they are symbols, personification, metaphors, etc.) and explain their effect.
- How does this atmosphere prepare us for the novel as a whole?

The character of Pip

- What is our initial impression of him? Think about character traits he seems to display.
- How does this prepare us for his actions later in the novel?

The character of Magwitch

- What is our initial impression of him?
- Make sure you mentioned things that suggest he is bad/not to be admired, and also elements that make us pity him.
- How does this introduction prepare us for his actions later in the novel?
- How does the final image of Magwitch as a corpse on temporary leave from the gibbet prepare us for Magwitch's fate at the end of the novel?

Dialogue, dialect and power

- How does the structure of the dialogue demonstrate the power relationship between the two characters?
- What is the importance of the fact that Magwitch uses dialect and that Pip does not?
- How do these words prepare for or contrast with their later relationship?

Themes

- What does the chapter suggest about at least **three** of these key themes?
  - Childhood – what sort of experience is childhood in this chapter and why? How about the experience of childhood (by Pip and others) in the book as a whole?
  - Money – how are wealth and poverty presented in this chapter and in the book as a whole? (i.e. good or bad?)
  - Crime – what is our initial impression of crime in the novel? How does this develop later on? (Think about which characters commit crimes in terms of the law, and other types of crimes committed in the novel.)
  - Love – is there any love in this chapter? Does this tally with the rest of the book? (Try to think of any characters who experience love positively.)
  - Class/snobbery – is there a class gap in this chapter? What about between them later in the novel? Why is this ironic? What does the whole novel suggest about snobbery?
  - Family – is there any sign of a functional family life at this stage of the novel? Are any families functional later in the novel? What is Dickens' overall message about families? Can you think of any that *are* functional?

For more on this topic see pages 76–77 of your Success Guide.

Total score / 19

How well did you do? ✗ 0–4 Try again 5–10 Getting there 11–15 Good work 16–19 Excellent! ✓

Literary technique (EN2)

A

Choose just one answer: a, b, c or d.

1 Round characters:
a) have symbolic significance
b) grow and develop during the course of a novel
c) are those characters that are seen from more than one point of view
d) are a bit like Mr Men characters **(1 mark)**

2 Dialogue is used in novels and short stories:
a) to break up long passages of description
b) because the reader does not know what the narrator looks like
c) because it can be vivid and realistic
d) to make novels more like plays **(1 mark)**

3 You should pay attention to the names of characters in novels because:
a) otherwise you will get confused
b) they sometimes provide clues about how the character will act
c) they sometimes have symbolic significance
d) authors think long and hard before naming their characters **(1 mark)**

4 A major disadvantage of using a first person narrator is:
a) that they can have a limited point of view
b) the reader has to trust them to tell the story
c) there is no suspense as you always know they will survive to tell the story
d) they can be irritating if you don't sympathise with them **(1 mark)**

5 A major disadvantage of using an omniscient narrator is:
a) they know too much and tend to appear in longer books
b) they are less realistic than first person narrators
c) they are more likely to digress
d) they are less reliable than first person narrators **(1 mark)**

Score / 5

B

Read the passage below and then answer the questions that follow.

Marley was dead: to begin with. There is no doubt whatever about that. The register of his burial was signed by the clergyman, the clerk, the undertaker, and the chief mourner. Scrooge signed it: and Scrooge's name was good upon 'Change, for anything he chose to put his hand to. Old Marley was as dead as a door-nail.

Mind! I don't mean to say that I know, of my own knowledge, what there is particularly dead about a door-nail. I might have been inclined, myself, to regard a coffin-nail as the deadest piece of ironmongery in the trade. But the wisdom of our ancestors is in the simile; and my unhallowed hands shall not disturb it, or the Country's done for. You will therefore permit me to repeat, emphatically, that Marley was as dead as a door-nail.

Scrooge knew he was dead? Of course he did. How could it be otherwise? Scrooge and he were partners for I don't know how many years. Scrooge was his sole executor, his sole administrator, his sole assign, his sole residuary legatee, his sole friend and sole mourner. And even Scrooge was not so dreadfully cut up by the sad event, but that he was an excellent man of business on the very day of the funeral, and solemnised it with an undoubted bargain.

A Christmas Carol **Charles Dickens**

1 What is surprising about the first sentence of this story?

....

.... **(1 mark)**

2 How well do these opening paragraphs set up a mood or tone for the story?

....

.... **(2 marks)**

3 How would you describe the tone?

....

.... **(1 mark)**

4 What does the digression about door-nails tell us about the story-teller?

....

.... **(2 marks)**

5 What conclusion about Marley's life does the third paragraph lead to?

....

.... **(2 marks)**

Score / 8

C This is an exam preparation question. Answer all parts of the question.

Analysing a novel or short story

Look at the opening few paragraphs of the novel you have been studying for GCSE.

Make notes on the topics mentioned in the spaces below.

Does it introduce the major characters? If so, how?
What description does the author give of the setting?
What indication is there of the themes that are to follow?
What plot developments are indicated?

Now write a brief paragraph that describes how well the opening of your novel works as an introduction to plot, character, setting and theme.

....

....

....

....

....

....

....

....

....

....

Score / 20

For more on this topic see pages 78–79 of your Success Guide.

Total score / 33

How well did you do? ✗ 0–7 Try again 8–17 Getting there 18–25 Good work 26–33 Excellent! ✓

Themes, mood, atmosphere (EN2)

A

Choose just one answer: a, b, c or d.

1 Novels can contain:
a) a moral or a theme but not both
b) only one theme
c) more than one theme
d) only one moral (1 mark)

2 A motif is:
a) a word or phrase that appears at the front of a novel
b) a recurring word, idea or image
c) a crucial moment in the plot
d) the reason why characters behave as they do (1 mark)

3 Novels generally use:
a) fewer literary devices than poems
b) more literary devices than poems
c) the same kinds of literary devices as poems but over more pages
d) a different set of literary devices from poems (1 mark)

4 One of the most significant literary differences between novels and short stories is:
a) short stories are shorter
b) short stories usually focus on a single incident or point in time
c) short stories use more literary devices
d) short stories have a sting in the tail (1 mark)

5 Short stories are probably less popular than novels because:
a) they have fewer characters
b) dialogue tends to be fragmented
c) they are too intense
d) people like to 'get lost' in novels (1 mark)

Score / 5

B

Read the passage below and then answer the questions that follow.

The passage is from near the end of a short story called 'The Gift of the Magi'. Two young people who are very poor but very much in love have sold their most precious possessions to buy gifts for each other.

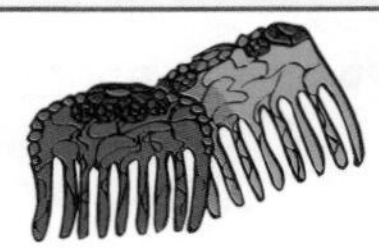

For there lay The Combs – the set of combs, side and back, that Della had worshipped long in a Broadway window. Beautiful combs, pure tortoise shell, with jewelled rims – just the shade to wear in the beautiful vanished hair. They were expensive combs, she knew, and her heart had simply craved and yearned over them without the least hope of possession. And now, they were hers, but the tresses that should have adorned the coveted adornments were gone.

But she hugged them to her bosom, and at length she was able to look up with dim eyes and a smile and say: 'My hair grows so fast, Jim!'

And then Della leaped up like a little singed cat and cried, 'Oh, oh!'

Jim had not yet seen his beautiful present. She held it out to him eagerly upon her open palm. The dull precious metal seemed to flash with a reflection of her bright and ardent spirit.

'Isn't it a dandy, Jim? I hunted all over town to find it. You'll have to look at the time a hundred times a day now. Give me your watch. I want to see how it looks on it.'

Instead of obeying, Jim tumbled down on the couch and put his hands under the back of his head and smiled.

'Dell,' said he, 'let's put our Christmas presents away and keep 'em a while. They're too nice to use just at present. I sold the watch to get the money to buy your combs. And now suppose you put the chops on.'

O Henry

1 What has Della sold to buy the watch chain?

....

.... (1 mark)

2 What has Jim sold to buy the combs?

....

.... (1 mark)

3 What is the problem for both of them?

....

.... (2 marks)

4 How would you describe the tone of this story?

....

.... (1 mark)

5 Do you think this makes a good ending to a short story? Give two reasons.

....

.... (2 marks)

Score / 6

C

This is an exam preparation question. Answer all parts of the question.

Analysing a short story

Choose a short story that you have studied that you think has an effective ending.

Use the spaces below to make notes on the topics mentioned.

Does it resolve the 'problem' of the story?
Does it provide a satisfactory conclusion for the character/s?
Does it bring the themes of the story into focus?
Does it leave you with something to think about?

Now write a paragraph that explains the effectiveness of the ending you have chosen.

....

....

....

....

....

....

....

....

....

....

For more on this topic see pages 80–81 of your Success Guide.

Total score / 11

How well did you do? 0–2 Try again 3–5 Getting there 6–8 Good work 9–11 Excellent!

Short stories

A

Choose just one answer: a, b, c or d.

1 The most popular areas for comparison of short stories are:
a) character and theme
b) plot and sub-plot
c) plot and character
d) theme and plot (1 mark)

2 When you are writing about short stories from different cultures which of the following might need more attention?
a) theme
b) character
c) setting
d) style (1 mark)

3 What should you avoid when writing about short stories in the exam?
a) treating them like poems
b) over-long quotations
c) stories by the same author
d) stories with contrasting themes (1 mark)

4 You need to revise all of the stories before the exam because:
a) in some years there will be no free choice of stories
b) you may want to refer to them in your essay
c) it is good revision practice
d) all the stories are interesting (1 mark)

5 A question on style would probably involve:
a) discussing the authors' plot devices
b) exploring such things as narrative technique, imagery and symbolism
c) a close examination of the differences between characters
d) a discussion of how well the authors planned their stories (1 mark)

Score / 5

B

Read and compare the two opening paragraphs of the two short stories below and then answer the questions that follow.

Dead Men's Path **Chinua Achebe**

Michael Obi's hopes were fulfilled much earlier than he had expected. He was appointed headmaster of Ndume Central School in January 1949. It had always been an unprogressive school, so the Mission authorities decided to send a young and energetic man to run it. Obi accepted this responsibility with enthusiasm. He had many wonderful ideas and this was an opportunity to put them into practice. He had had sound secondary school education which designated him a "pivotal teacher" in the official records and set him apart from the other headmasters in the mission field. He was outspoken in his condemnation of the narrow views of these older and often less-educated ones.

Games at Twilight **Anita Desai**

It was still too hot to play outdoors. They had had their tea, they had been washed and had their hair brushed, and after the long day of confinement in the house that was not cool but at least a protection from the son, the children strained to get out. Their faces were red and bloated with the effort, but their mother would not open the door, everything was still curtained and shuttered in a way that stifled the children, made them feel that their lungs were stuffed with cotton wool and their noses with dust and if they didn't burst out into the light and see the sun and feel the air, they would choke.

1 What is the mood of *Dead Men's Path*?

....

.... (1 mark)

2 How is it established?

....

.... (2 marks)

3 What is the mood of *Games at Twilight*?

....

.... (1 mark)

4 How is it established?

....

.... (2 marks)

5 What is the difference between the narrative points of view of the two stories?

....

.... (2 marks)

6 How well do they lead into the rest of the stories?

....

.... (2 marks)

Score / 10

C

This is a GCSE-style question.

Comparing short stories

Choose two short stories that you have studied. How well have they given you an insight into other times and places?

The key words in this question are 'how well', 'insight' and 'other times and places'.

Use these words to plan an essay using either a spider diagram (see page 57) or a table (see page 63).

For more on this topic see pages 82–83 of your Success Guide.

Total score / 15

How well did you do? 0–3 Try again 4–8 Getting there 9–12 Good work 13–15 Excellent!

Exam technique

A

Choose just one answer: a, b, c or d.

1 How will bringing two spare pens to the exam help to relieve your stress?

a) you can drum on the table with them if you get bored
b) you won't have to worry about your pen running out
c) you can lend one to a friend
d) you can write in different colours **(1 mark)**

2 How many times should you read passages in exams?

a) once, making notes as you go
b) once to make maximum use of the time
c) twice – first to get the general meaning and then to collect evidence
d) twice – first to get the general meaning and second as a safety check **(1 mark)**

3 In an exam essay:

a) a full introduction is essential
b) introductions are unnecessary
c) brief introductions are advisable
d) the introduction should fully outline the rest of the essay **(1 mark)**

4 The marks for each question shown on the exam paper:

a) should be used as guidance on the length of your answer
b) are for examiners' use only
c) tell you how many points you must make
d) can show you whether part of an answer is important or not **(1 mark)**

5 If a question asks you to 'explain', you should:

a) present a logical argument
b) use persuasive language
c) write in Standard English
d) give a detailed account **(1 mark)**

Score /5

B

Read the passage below and then answer the questions that follow.

In the Western world being a vegetarian is usually a matter of choice. As a joke some vegetarians say that they eat vegetables not because of sympathy for animals but because they really hate plants. Some people are vegetarians because of their religious beliefs, but most people choose to become vegetarians because of their ideas about animals. The thought that a living, breathing, feeling creature has to be murdered just so that people can eat is too much for most vegetarians. They think that the killing of helpless animals is both unnecessary and unfair.

As the world's population increases and the world's energy supplies diminish, the production of meat for food is becoming unacceptably expensive and inefficient. A kilo of beef, for instance, is TEN TIMES more expensive to produce than a kilo of wheat. Meat production also uses up more energy than it produces. The most energy efficient meat farming gives an energy return of only 34.5 per cent whereas even the least energy efficient plant food gives a return of 328 per cent.

1 What kind of text is this?

....

.... (1 mark)

2 Write down one fact and one opinion from this passage.

....

.... (2 marks)

3 What methods are used to persuade in the first paragraph?

....

.... (2 marks)

4 What methods are used to persuade in the second paragraph?

....

.... (2 marks)

5 Identify one typographical feature used to add emphasis in this passage.

....

.... (1 mark)

Score /8

C This is a GCSE-style question. Answer one question on separate paper.

The following are the type of questions that might appear in the writing section of your exam. Choose **one** and spend an hour writing a response.

1 Write an article for a teenage magazine in which you **argue** the case *either* for *or* against vegetarianism.

2 A friend is thinking of becoming a vegetarian.

Either: write a letter in which you try to **persuade** your friend to become a vegetarian.
Or: write a letter in which you try to **dissuade** your friend from becoming a vegetarian.

3 People sometimes complain that vegetarian meals can be boring.

Write an article for the cookery section of a magazine that instructs readers on how to cook an interesting and appetising vegetarian meal.

Score / 18

For more on this topic see pages 86–89 of your Success Guide.

Total score / 31

How well did you do? ✗ 0–10 Try again 11–18 Getting there 19–24 Good work 24–31 Excellent! ✓

GCSE Practice Paper 1

Text 1

your old mobile to Oxfam

Why recycle mobile phones?

Apart from the fact that old handsets can be used to raise funds for Oxfam's humanitarian work around the world, donating old mobile phones to Oxfam is good because they can be recycled. Mobiles should not be disposed of thoughtlessly, because the batteries contain dangerous chemicals and because many of the materials in the phone can be reused. The most harmful chemicals in the batteries are heavy metals, such as nickel and lithium, which are toxic and not biodegradable. Buried deep in the earth, these metals could, in the future, seep into underground rivers and other water sources. Surprisingly though, the law still allows for them to be disposed of in landfill sites. Phones donated to Oxfam are refurbished and sold, raising money for our work overseas. Many of them will eventually be exported to regions with expanding mobile phone networks. These second-hand phones are usually more affordable for people there than new ones would be. The few batteries and phones which cannot be reused are sent for reprocessing, so that toxins are extracted and any materials left are reused.

Oxfam's **Bring Bring** appeal will help protect the environment, as well as benefiting people in developing countries.

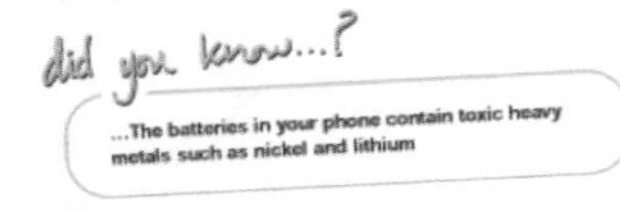

The mobile phone revolution

The first mobile phones were produced in the USA in the late 1970s, but they were heavy and unreliable. Mobile phones as we know them now appeared in the mid-1990s, and since then, they have grown enormously in popularity and have changed the way we communicate. It is now possible to speak to people in remote corners of the world where normal telephone technology is relatively undeveloped – or perhaps non-existent. A new form of communication has come into existence: the txt msg. This is particularly popular in some European countries, including the UK and Finland. Almost one billion text messages are sent each month in the UK.

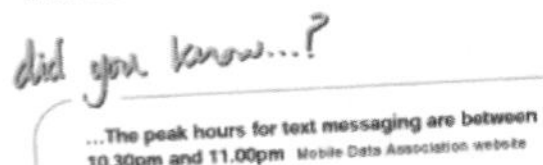

What is a mobile phone made of?

A mobile phone is a technological miracle. Thirty years ago, you would have needed a whole room for this equipment. Today, it fits inside the handset. A mobile phone consists of seven main parts:

- **circuit board containing several computer chips**
- **antenna**
- **liquid crystal display**
- **microphone**
- **keyboard**
- **speaker**
- **battery**

In effect, a mobile phone is a type of two-way radio.

brng yr old mbl 2 Oxfm –
U know it mks snse

Photo: Brian Moody

Activities

Here are some ways of taking your thoughts further

1. Prepare an assembly on mobile phones in order to raise money for Oxfam and to get your fellow pupils thinking about the way we communicate.
2. Is it important for everyone to have access to technology? What disadvantages do people suffer if they don't have access to the internet, e-mail, or mobile phones, or if they haven't learned how to use the technology? Should governments give computers to poorer people? Should we in the industrialised world provide technology for people in the developing world? Write a piece about your thoughts on these issues.
3. Try and find out about the way people communicate in other countries, and the way people communicated in the past. Talk to your teacher about how to make contact with people abroad. It is often better to communicate with people in developing countries by letter or fax (e-mails can be difficult for them to receive, because they take a long time to download). You could also think of the books you've read that are set in the past.
4. Rewrite a well-known story, showing how events would have turned out if mobile phones had been available. (For example, Cinderella texts her fairy godmother when her sisters have gone to the ball...use your imagination.)
5. Make a leaflet giving advice to young people about making the best use of their mobile phones. You could include tips on not spending too much money on calls, taking health precautions, communicating in other ways (face to face, letters, etc), staying safe from bullies and muggers, as well as some of the plus points of the phones (staying in contact with your friends, easy access to information, etc).
6. Draw up a cost–benefit sheet for a mobile phone. Make a list of all the costs involved on one side, and all the benefits that people get from the phone on the other. Are there any 'social costs' (eg health risks)? Is it worth the money? What might people have to do without in order to afford a phone?

Useful resources

How your phone works

Encarta Encyclopedia:
http://encarta.msn.co.uk
(search under 'Cellular Radio Telephone')

How Stuff Works:
www.howstuffworks.com/cell-phone.htm

Inventors:
http://inventors.about.com/library/weekly/aa070899.htm

Issues about phones, and phones around the world

http://news.bbc.co.uk *(search for 'mobile phone')* or search for 'mobile phone' on the site of any reputable newspaper or periodical.

Texting

www.text.it

For extra materials and worksheets connected with Oxfam's **Bring Bring** scheme, visit www.oxfam.org.uk/coolplanet. Cool Planet also features information and activities for young people and resources and ideas for teachers.

For further information about resources for schools which bring a global dimension to life in the classroom, send for a copy of Oxfam's catalogue *Oxfam Education Resources for Schools.*

Contact
Oxfam Supporter Services,
274 Banbury Road, Oxford OX2 7DZ

Tel: (01865) 312610

e-mail: oxfam@oxfam.org.uk

Oxfam

Text 2

Saturday October 19, 2002 • *The* **Guardian**

What's your poison?

Many gadgets contain nasty chemicals and will never biodegrade. So, can we covet them and love the environment, too? Oliver Bennett investigates

The concept of "planned obsolescence" created a huge stir when it was first identified by Vance Packard in his 1960 book *The Waste Makers*. Packard's theory was that manufacturers designed products to have a short life, thereby committing us to a constant cycle of consumption.

Four decades on, we are in the age of junk electronics as never before. Today's technology is so transient it goes from shelf to bin in a matter of months. The average computer is changed every two years, the typical mobile phone every 18 months. Two million televisions are trashed every year. Yet, the pressure to buy new stuff is enormous – What! You haven't got a digital widescreen TV yet? Loser!

While the idea of being a responsible consumer is nice in principle, many of us are too wedded to buying the latest gadgets. Mike Childs, a senior campaigner at Friends Of The Earth, understands this human instinct to acquire, but reckons that we need to resist it. "We should step back and ask ourselves: what are the implications of buying these things?" he says. If buy we must, then manufacturers should design hardware that "can be upgraded rather than changed" and be penalised if they do not "design out waste".

Some companies are taking note. Honda and Toyota have adopted a catch-all recycling strategy known as "zero waste" – something also practised by New Zealand, the cities of Canberra and Toronto and some UK local authorities, such as Bath and North East Somerset Council.

But what about us lowly punters? There are few options for what to do with old technology. It's often not worth repairing, and anyway, there are few repairers left. The second-hand market has crashed: schools and charity shops have been inundated. So old equipment gathers dust in lofts and cupboards, in what Sarah Bond, of recycling company Shields Environmental, calls "home landfill".

We are caught between two stools. On one hand, waste directives mean that we now can't dump certain items, even if we wanted to: old televisions and PCs are now proscribed as potentially hazardous, each bearing a kilo or two of lead. Yet, on the other hand, there isn't a systematic route for responsible disposal.

Coming soon, though, is the Waste Electrical and Electronic Equipment (WEEE) Directive, due to pass through the European Parliament by 2004. This will oblige manufacturers and retailers to take back for recycling all the TVs, stereos, *et al*, they've sold.

And, slowly, things are beginning to happen here. For example, Shields Environmental recently launched Fonebak, a mobile phone recycling scheme, where you send in dud phones or take them back to a participating store. Fifteen million mobiles are replaced each year in the UK, each with the potential to leach nasty contaminants. "The worst ones are the old 'bricks'," says Sarah Bond. "A battery from one of these is enough to pollute 600,000 litres of water with cadmium." With Fonebak, metals are extracted and re-deployed; some phones are "remanufactured" to sell in developing countries; and casings are incinerated for power supply.

In tiny ways, we can already prevent gadget waste. There are several places to buy eco-friendly electronics (see left). Mainstream companies are getting in on the act, too. Consumers can choose solar-powered gizmos – calculators, radios, watches; or they can use rechargeable and recycled batteries. Panasonic uses lead-free solder; Sony has " greened" its latest Walkman/radio with decomposable "plastic" made from corn. There's even a growing range of green gimmicks: clockwork torches, clocks powered by potatoes and mouse mats made of recycled tyres.

Will this create a new glut of eco-friendly junk? Possibly. But at least today's wastemakers will have to be more responsible than those before.

From http://www.guardian.co.uk/weekend/story/0,3605,813517,00.html

1 Read the Oxfam leaflet.

You are being asked to follow an argument, select material appropriate to a purpose and tell the difference between fact and opinion.

a) Write down one opinion from page one of the leaflet.

....

.... **(2 marks)**

b) Write down one fact from the main text of the leaflet.

....

.... **(2 marks)**

c) How does the leaflet use facts to persuade people to recycle their mobiles?

....

....

....

....

....

....

....

.... **(6 marks)**

2 **Now read the article from *The Guardian* 'What's your poison?'**

Explain in your own words some of the things that ordinary people can do to increase the recycling of consumer products.

(6 marks)

3 **You are now being asked to read the texts as media texts.**

a) What do the text and images chosen for Text 1 (the leaflet) tell you about its target audience?

(4 marks)

b) What features of the layout and presentation of the leaflet help it to reach its target audience?

(4 marks)

c) What techniques does Text 2 (the newspaper article) use to get and hold its readers' attention?

(3 marks)

Score / 27

GCSE Practice Paper 2

Text 1

Home. A place of conker love and clamper van hate. Where we invent the best sports in the world then get good at playing them badly. At Home we like to do ourselves down but we're pretty plucky when we want to be. We are John Lennon. We are the Suffragettes. We are the man who invented the bobble hat. Come out of the cold, have a cup of tea and make yourself at Home because it's good here.

Text 2

What is Britishness anyway?

Apart from the sea, what keeps the British together?

David Blunkett has named academic Professor Sir Bernard Crick as the man who will set up a controversial "Britishness" test for would-be immigrants. Part of the problem might be there are so many definitions of what "Britishness" is.

Mr Blunkett's plans for citizenship tests – and his plain speaking approach on immigration and race – have led to accusations of borderline racism from some on the left.

He was warned when the tests were announced that his comments could be exploited by racists, and he has been criticised for showing a "distinct lack of understanding".

It's an illustration of how delicate a subject race still is.

Views on best of Britishness

Sophie Dahl: *"Earl Grey and John Galliano"*

Elton John: *"Sense of humour"*

Andrew Motion: *"Beer on tap"*

Norman Cook: *"Most people speak your language when you go abroad"*

Denise Lewis: *"Gin and tonic"*

Many have tried to define what it means to be British, sometimes in relation to race but often at the level of the constituent parts of the United Kingdom.

For former Tory chairman Norman Tebbit, it was the infamous "cricket test" which mattered. Immigrant communities, he said, should support England even when it was playing their country of origin. Many objected to having their loyalties called into question.

Commenting on Professor Crick's appointment, Lord Tebbit told BBC News Online the "cricket test" was "not a test of Britishness it was a test of integration".

"Nobody used to talk about Britishness in the 1940s and 1950s, it is a phenomenon of large numbers of non-British people coming into the country".

"The question is about foreigners and how foreigners are persuaded to adopt British customs and styles."

He said England cricket captain Nasser Hussain – who was born in India – was a good example of racial integration.

'Long shadows on county grounds'

Lord Tebbit went on: "My father's family came to Britain in the 16th Century, but I regard the Anglo-Saxon period, King Alfred and William the Conqueror are part of my inheritance."

He said the challenge will be to "persuade these people (immigrants) that Waterloo, Trafalgar and the Battle of Britain, are part of their heritage."

John Major also attempted to define Britishness, although more in an attempt to reassure those worried at EU influence than immigration.

He said that in 50 years' time, it would still be the country of "long shadows on county grounds, warm beer, invincible green suburbs, dog lovers and pools fillers and – as George Orwell said 'old maids bicycling to holy communion through the morning mist'."

Same hymn sheet?

David Blunkett mentioned two things in particular – forced marriages and genital mutilation – which he said were certainly not part of Britishness.

But stating in any detail what are characteristic of Britishness is a challenging task.

Would there, for instance, be cultural harmony in a massive jamming session between a garage collective, a colliery band, drumming Orangemen, and a chamber orchestra – all of them distinctly British in their own way?

Finding the common ground which defines a nation is a challenge for many countries, especially as the concept of the "nation state" comes into question from the rise of international bodies and multi-national companies.

Roots

Within the UK, devolution in Scotland, Wales and Northern Ireland, inspired much soul-searching about what – if anything – it meant to be British. As the devolved assemblies settle in, there are also moves for the English regions to have more autonomy.

What exemplifies Britishness? In a recent survey, 91% said it was the NHS. The concept of modern Britain was founded in 1707 with the Act of Union which brought England and Scotland together.

In just over five years' time, it will in a sense be Britain's 300th anniversary. But it may well be that without a greater sense of what constitutes Britishness, any celebrations will struggle to be a success in the public's mind.

From http://news.bbc.co.uk/1/hi/uk/1701843.stm

1 Read the UKTV advertisement.

You are being asked to follow an argument, select material appropriate to a purpose and tell the difference between fact and opinion.

a) Write down one statement that relates to people's opinions about the UK.

....

....

....

.... **(3 marks)**

b) Write down one statement that relates to facts about people from the UK.

(3 marks)

c) How does the advertisement use stereotypes to encourage people to identify themselves as being from the UK?

(3 marks)

2 Now read the article from BBC web page, 'What is Britishness anyway?'

Use your own words to explain three opinions about what it is to be British used in the body of the page.

(6 marks)

3 You are now being asked to read the texts as media texts.

a) Why do you think that the advertisers chose a combination of a dinosaur and two old ladies as the main image for this ad? How does the image reinforce the message of the text?

(4 marks)

b) Explain how this advertisement is attempting to establish a brand rather than advertising a particular product.

(4 marks)

c) What techniques does the web page article use to get and hold attention and to 'add value' to the main article? How effective are these techniques?

(4 marks)

Score /27

GCSE Practice Paper 3

Text 1

Hollywood ending flaws Leo's diamond war story

Certificate: 15 Rating: ★★★☆☆

The trouble with Hollywood is that when it gets hold of a serious subject, it feels impelled to dress its argument up either as an action movie or a love story, in case we all get bored. It's understandable but frustrating.

Ed Zwick's film, set in the battle-torn Sierra Leone of the Nineties, is about the trade in 'blood diamonds', sold on the market after discovery by put-upon African workers so that war and mayhem can continue to be financed. Its central character is Danny, Leonardo DiCaprio's Zimbabwean ex-mercenary. He's presented to us as a man without scruples, making a convenient bargain with Djimon Hounsou's excellently played villager who has been taken from his family and forced to work in the diamond fields.

The bargain is that DiCaprio will help him find his wife and children, one of whom has been forced by the rebels to become a child soldier, if Hounsou will lead him to the rare pink diamond he has found and hidden in the fields.

So far, so good. Eduardo Serra, the cinematographer who made The Girl With The Pearl Earring look like a painting by a Dutch master, this time portrays Sierra Leone as a beautiful country being destroyed by a civil war of appalling ferocity, in which children are forced to play their part and limbs are lopped off without compunction.

And Zwick, assembling his cast largely from Africans, watches a number of convincing if sometimes horrendous cameos.

This, one thinks at one point, is the US version of The Constant Gardener. Then we get Jennifer Connelly as an impossibly pretty American journalist trying to persuade DiCaprio to mend his ways, and we see the Zimbabwean begin to see the light.

In the end, he's a changed man and in love. But the film is also changed, and not for the better.

What remains is a comparatively honest effort from Hollywood but one fatally weakened by the familiar scent of compromise in its final reels.

The plus point is that it has caused those who might be thought guilty of the blood diamond trade to issue all sorts of disclaimers. That, at least, is a strong point in its favour.

Text 2

There's a lot to think about as you look for that special diamond. It's a once in a lifetime purchase, and you want to make sure your diamond is one that you and your loved one will cherish forever.

You may hear it's the 4Cs of colour, cut, clarity and carat weight that matter. But there is one more 'C' to ask about before making your purchase, and it stands for conflict. Did you know that some diamonds have helped fund devastating civil wars in Africa, destroying the lives of millions?

This guide tells you what you need to know about the trade in conflict diamonds. And most importantly, what you can do to try and make sure that the diamonds you buy are conflict-free. As a customer, you can really make a difference and help make sure the diamond industry is keeping its promises to end the trade in conflict diamonds. Diamonds may be expensive, but they shouldn't cost lives.

Help stop the trade in conflict diamonds. Ask for conflict-free.

Rebel soldiers on patrol in Côte d'Ivoire

What are conflict diamonds?

Conflict diamonds are those sold in order to fund armed conflict and civil war. Profits from the trade in conflict diamonds, worth billions of dollars, were used by warlords and rebels to buy arms during the devastating wars in Angola, the Democratic Republic of Congo (DRC), Liberia and Sierra Leone. Wars which have cost an estimated 3.7 million lives.

While the wars in Angola, Liberia and Sierra Leone are now over, and fighting in the DRC has decreased, the problem of conflict diamonds hasn't gone away. Diamonds mined in rebel-held areas in Côte d'Ivoire, a West African country in the midst of a volatile conflict, are reaching the international diamond market. Conflict diamonds from Liberia are also being smuggled into neighbouring countries and exported as part of the legitimate diamond trade.

International efforts to stop the trade – the Kimberley Process

In 2003, an international certification scheme called the Kimberley Process was launched, making it illegal to trade in conflict diamonds. A Kimberley Process certificate, guaranteeing diamonds as conflict-free, accompanies all official shipments of rough diamonds to and from participating countries.

To support this, the international diamond industry agreed to a voluntary system of warranties to ensure diamonds continued to be tracked right up to the point of sale. All invoices for the sale of diamonds and jewellery containing diamonds should now include a written guarantee that states they are conflict-free.

What the diamond industry agreed to do

- Include a written guarantee on all invoices
- Adopt a code of conduct to prevent the buying or selling of conflict diamonds
- Train staff about company policies and government regulations
- Keep records of all invoices and have them audited every year

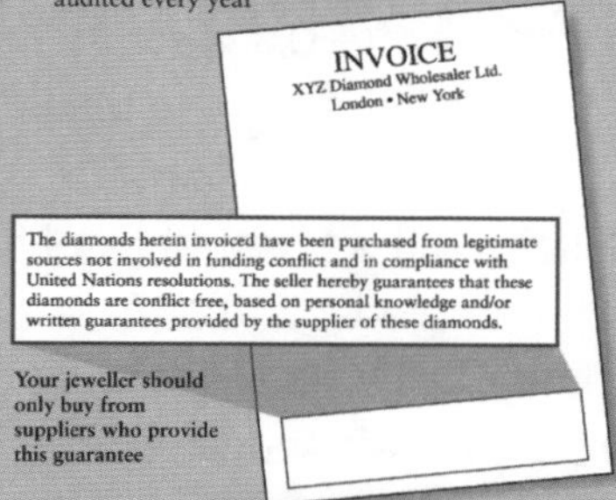

Your jeweller should only buy from suppliers who provide this guarantee

READING: NON-FICTION AND MEDIA

'Hollywood ending flaws Leo's diamond war story' is a film review from *The Daily Mail* newspaper.

Guide to Buying Diamonds is a leaflet produced by human rights organisation Amnesty International UK. http://www.amnesty.org.uk/business

Read both texts carefully, and then answer question 1 and question 2 on separate sheets of paper.

These answers will be marked for reading. Plan your answers and write them carefully.

1 Read the film review, 'Hollywood ending flaws Leo's diamond war story'.

Using the review, explain how the film *Blood Diamond* treats the issue of blood diamonds indicating what is good and what is bad about this treatment.

Write no more than 2 or 3 paragraphs. Use your own words as far as possible.

(20 marks)

2 Read the leaflet, *Guide to Buying Diamonds.*

What do you think is the writer's purpose in writing this leaflet, and how well is it achieved?

In your answer, you should comment on the content, language and presentation of the leaflet.

(20 marks)

GCSE model answers – PAPER 1

1 a) 'A mobile phone is a technological miracle' or 'U know it mks snse' **(2 marks)**

b) Any fact apart from the ones in 'did you know?' boxes will do. For instance 'The first mobile phones were produced in the US in the seventies.' **(2 marks)**

c) The leaflet uses facts to persuade people to recycle their mobiles in several ways. First of all it points out that to not recycle your phone is bad for the environment. It then goes on to tell the reader how mobile phones have made people's lives better in the developed world. The leaflet assumes that the readers will be interested in mobiles and so it provides simple information about how mobile phones work. On the second page of the leaflet the facts relate more closely to Oxfam and its role in the developing world. The leaflet covers three main points in this section: how difficult communication was before mobiles; how mobiles have improved people's lives; and how mobiles help in disaster relief. In addition to all of this information the leaflet is decorated with 'did you know?' boxes that are filled with less relevant but quite interesting pieces of information. The leaflet is trying to persuade people to recycle their mobile phones either to raise money for Oxfam or so the phones can be reused in the developing world. All the information provided helps the reader to understand why this idea 'mks snse'. **(6 marks)**

2 First of all we should buy hardware that can be upgraded rather than having to be replaced or choose products that have a 'zero waste' policy. Two things that used to be sensible were repairing things rather than throwing them away and giving things to charity. Unfortunately there are few repairers left and schools and charities have too much to sell nowadays. We can use a service like 'Fonebak' to recycle mobile phones and prevent them from harming the environment. We can also choose solar-powered calculators, radios or watches or use rechargeable and recycled batteries. Finally we can buy 'green' products like clockwork torches, potato-powered clocks or mouse mats made from recycled tyres. **(6 marks)**

3 a) This leaflet is obviously aimed at a young audience; the sort of people who use and are interested in mobile phones. The leaflet is meant to be friendly and informal – you can tell this from the style of typography used in the title – it looks like something a young person might produce with a marker pen. The title is also meant to be a joke as 'bring bring' is what the leaflet is asking people to do and it is also the noise made by some phones. The information in the leaflet is quite serious but it is presented in short bursts so as not to put people off. Also there are little pieces of trivia in the 'did you know?' boxes that help to maintain interest. Although the audience is young people the leaflet does not patronise its audience by being too simple or too trendy – except possibly in its use of text messages. The image chosen shows young people, things that young people find interesting or, in the case of the picture of Dom Jolly, that the target audience finds amusing. **(4 marks)**

b) The layout and presentation of the leaflet is well suited to its young target audience. The main text is presented in short, easily read bursts of information each of which is clearly labelled with a sub-heading. The main heading and the 'did you know?' boxes are presented in an informal hand-written style that might have been produced by a young person in the first place. The illustrations break up the text and are of things like mobile phones, well-known comedians and attractive young people. **(4 marks)**

c) The newspaper article's main attention grabber is its headline, 'What's your poison?'
This is quite a striking phrase but it is also familiar because it is sometimes used when people are offering a choice of food or drink. It turns out that the article is actually about poison but the reader has to investigate the article a little further to find this out. The second technique that

the article uses is the sub-heading. This explains what the article is about but is also designed to increase reader curiosity as it contains a question. The language of the sub-heading is quite informal, using words like 'nasty' rather than, say, 'dangerous' or 'environmentally challenging'. The body of the article continues in an informal tone. It uses words like 'trash' and 'bin' and it even imagines a conversation 'What! You haven't got a digital widescreen TV yet? Loser!' The article seems to assume that people might be put off if a serious subject was taken too seriously. **(3 marks)**

GCSE model answers – PAPER 2

1 a) People love conkers. Or people hate clamper vans. Or we like to do ourselves down. Or we are plucky when we want to be. **(3 marks)**

b) John Lennon, or the Suffragettes or the man who invented the bobble hat are from the UK. **(3 marks)**

c) The advertisement begins with statements about 'UK' type opinions. These are almost inevitably stereotypes as the advertisers want to make a general statement about people in the UK that will not offend people. The conkers idea is meant to remind people of their happy childhood and the clamper van comment relates to shared adult annoyances. The statement about sports is a familiar one to explain UK teams' lack of success in games like soccer, cricket and rugby. The comments on doing ourselves down and pluck are meant to remind people of attitudes in the Second World War. If the advertisers had not used stereotypes, people would start disagreeing with the statements and would not be inclined to identify with UKTV. **(3 marks)**

2 Some people have tried to define Britishness in terms of race. Norman Tebbit's 'cricket test' was based on the idea that people who have come to live in Britain should support England even when it was playing their 'home' country. John Major used images of the past and of relaxed summers to define Britishness. He hardly mentions towns or cities at all but he does say that people like to do the football pools and love dogs. David Blunkett did not say what was British but said that things like forced marriages and genital mutilation were definitely un-British. **(6 marks)**

3 a) The idea that the advertisers seem to be aiming for in the text is a combination of the familiar and the slightly odd or eccentric. This makes the choice of picture very appropriate, as it shows two little old ladies at the seaside in what for many people will be a familiar image. In the background, however, there is a very strange dinosaur. No explanation is given and so the two parts of the photograph produce the same combination of familiar and odd that we find in the text. **(4 marks)**

b) We can tell that this ad is for a brand because it is not for any specific product or even programme. The logos at the bottom all have the initials UK in them and so the ad is trying to define what the idea of UK means to most people. Presumably the advertisers are implying that if you watch enough UKTV channels you will get a mixture of familiar and slightly odd programmes. **(4 marks)**

c) The article itself uses many of the techniques of ordinary newspapers. The headline uses a question to grab the readers' attention and there are a number of sub-headings to catch the readers' eyes and draw them further into the article. The article begins with the important facts and then provides plenty of examples to broaden the discussion. The added value is contained in the boxes around the story and in the images used. The quotations from famous people are interesting in a gossipy kind of way and the picture of the cricket screen illustrates something that people might not understand from John Major's discussion of Britishness. The boxes and pictures are generally useful in widening the range of opinions expressed in the article and giving the whole thing more balance. **(4 marks)**

GCSE answers – PAPER 3

1 Main points will include:

Good points: serious subject; realistic setting; graphic violence; excellent acting; honest effort to deal with a serious subject; provoked a reaction from diamond traders

Bad points: imposed love story; impossibly pretty heroine; change in tone of the film; compromised ending

(2 marks for each point made)

2 Main points will include:

Purpose – to make diamond buyers aware of the issue of conflict diamonds – to help them to buy diamonds responsibly

Content – explains about things to look for – the four Cs – adds another C for 'conflict'.

Explains what conflict diamonds do – supporting wars – explains how diamond sellers have responded

Language – quiet and understated – does not wish to upset people who may be buying diamonds for a special occasion

Presentation – image of beauty of diamond contrasts with image of soldiers – image used of proper certification – message on ring – simple advice in larger type (ask for conflict free) – bullet points on diamond industry agreement

Your own assessment of how well purpose achieved

(1 mark for each point made and 5 marks for a sensible assessment)